BRED
TO RUN

ALSO BY MIKE HELM

A Breed Apart:
The Horses and the Players (1991)

Mike Helm

BRED TO RUN

The Making of a
Thoroughbred

A John Macrae Book
HENRY HOLT AND COMPANY
NEW YORK

Henry Holt and Company, Inc.
Publishers since 1866
115 West 18th Street
New York, New York 10011

Henry Holt ® is a registered
trademark of Henry Holt and Company, Inc.

Published in Canada by Fitzhenry & Whiteside Ltd.,
195 Allstate Parkway, Markham, Ontario L3R 4T8.

Library of Congress Cataloging-in-Publication Data

Helm, Mike.
    Bred to run : the making of a thoroughbred / Mike Helm.—1st ed.
       p.   cm.
    "A John Macrae book."
    1. Thoroughbred horse—Breeding. 2. Race horses—Breeding.
I. Title.
SF293.T5H42   1993   93-28376
636.1'2—dc20   CIP
ISBN 0-8050-2144-2

Henry Holt books are available for special promotions
and premiums. For details contact:
Director, Special Markets.

First Edition—1993

DESIGNED BY LUCY ALBANESE

10 9 8 7 6 5 4 3 2 1

For Jesse

CONTENTS

CONTENTS

PREFACE

Horse racing is an old story. Though we don't have a reliable birth date, there is ample evidence to suggest that the sport followed the horse's domestication by not many years. And betting on the outcome, as any handicapper knows, could not have been far behind. Several thousand years later, in the seventeenth century, members of the English nobility raised the ante by introducing Thoroughbreds. The sport of kings was the result.

In 1992 more than $10 billion flowed through the pari-mutuel windows in North America, with $770 million of that sum awarded to Thoroughbred owners and breeders whose annual charge it is to produce 35,000 foals. Of these, three percent will become stakes horses and only one will hit the ultimate jackpot and win the Kentucky Derby.

American racing fans, for their part, have generally paid scant attention to breeding and bloodlines. Imbued with the democratic ethos and having lost more than a few dollars on royally bred flops, they are quick to point out that some of the greatest racehorses— Kelso, Forego, and John Henry—established their class, not on the basis of pedigree, but with consistent performance on the track while carrying high weights.

Still, play enough races and, if only by osmosis, the alert handicapper begins to notice that certain bloodlines do in fact pass on specific attributes that can come home at a price. The progeny of Mr. Prospector, for example, tend toward speed and precocity, those of Nijinsky II excel on the turf, and the female descendants of Buckpasser and Ribot often add toughness and stamina to a pedigree. Within the drama of each race, the realization gradually takes hold that breeders are playing an even higher-priced game with the gene pool of the breed, and that every horse has been bred with a specific intent that racing fans ignore at their peril.

Yet, when it comes to breeding superior racehorses, nature does not reveal its secrets easily, and the theories of breeders, like the systems of handicappers, are destined to be wrong more often than they're right.

Given that every breeding and every horse race remains a chance, one truth continues to prevail—horses bred and raised in Kentucky consistently outperform all others. So, why not, I concluded, journey there and hang out with the real professionals whose daily responsibility it is to breed and raise the best horses we wager on? Why not see what it is they actually do, and test the validity of various breeding theories against the crucible of their practical experience?

And just as important, once in the Bluegrass, to pay close attention to the horses themselves. For while the Thoroughbred is the product of human will and selection, it is also a sentient creature with laws of its own that in turn subtly influences everything from the language to the mythology of its masters.

What follows is primarily an account of the activities at Claiborne Farm in Paris, Kentucky, during the breeding season of 1992, enriched by numerous conversations with other breeders and pedigree students throughout North America. I would particularly like to thank

Seth Hancock for giving me free rein at Claiborne; Dr. Deb Bennett for her help on the early history of the horse; and David Heckerman at *Thoroughbred Times*; Theresa Fitzgerald at *The Blood-Horse*; and Jack Werk at *Owner/Breeder*; without whose collective help and encouragement *Bred to Run* might never have been completed. Any errors in fact or judgment are, of course, finally my own.

—Mike Helm
May 1993

1

SETTING
THE STAGE

*I*t was the third week in February and just the beginning of the breeding season. A light winter drizzle angled down on the brown and still-dormant Kentucky bluegrass that, come spring, would turn lush and verdigris. Out in their paddocks Danzig, Mr. Prospector, Nijinsky II, and the other Claiborne stallions stood stoically with their backs to the wind, while tiny beads of dew congealed on the tips of their whiskers.

Thanks to modern horsepower, I had caught the red-eye express from San Francisco to Cincinnati the previous evening, rented a car, and undulated my way south over eighty miles of rolling hills to the heart of the bluegrass country in central Kentucky where I was now, at eleven o'clock on a Sunday morning, listening to John Sosby bend my ear. An ebullient, bearish man in his mid-fifties, Sosby has been assistant manager at Claiborne for the past eighteen years and has the day-to-day responsibility of running the farm.

Part Kentucky farm boy, part corporate manager, John Sosby is a lot like Claiborne itself. "This is a working horse farm," he assured me. "This isn't a place where somebody pours in millions of dollars just for a hobby. It's got to pay its own way, if we're gonna make it. I think you'll see over the next five days that from Seth Hancock on down we're basically hardworking, traditional people here. We don't have to window polish or shine for anybody. There's no flashing neon lights out front saying this is Claiborne. My father went to work here when I was three years old, in 1941. I grew up here and have worked here all my life. And it's been that way with Seth Hancock and his father before him and his grandfather before that. I've seen four generations of Hancocks. We've been successful doing things our way, so we're not gonna change for the sake of change. But we're willing to try something new if you can show us it's a better way."

I was at America's most famous horse farm because Seth Hancock, the lanky forty-three-year-old president of Claiborne, had invited me. Or, more accurately, because he had responded generously to my request that I spend a week at the farm in order to give racing fans an inside look at the breeding side of the sport. In fact, Seth was putting me up in the "Bullpen"—a stone and wooden-beamed cabin his father, A. B. "Bull" Hancock, had fancied enough to buy from a neighbor and reassemble as a place where he and his friends could gather to drink bourbon, swap stories, and smoke cigars. After graduating from the University of Kentucky, Seth had even lived in it for a few years. Centrally located, the Bullpen has muskets mounted on its walls that lend a touch of the Confederacy to it. Adding to the cabin's charm is the fact that once you press down on the wrought-iron latch and step past the oak-planked front door, you are little more than a three-minute lick downhill to the breeding shed where the stallions hold forth or a five-minute chug uphill to the foaling barn where the brood-mares give birth.

Claiborne, of course, doesn't exist in a vacuum. The farm is located in Bourbon County, just outside the town of Paris, some fourteen miles west of Lexington in the heart of Baptist country. Like many small rural towns, Paris is in the throes of a difficult transition. It has one foot in its agricultural past—mostly corn, tobacco, horses, and livestock—and another in the declining industrial base of the 1990s that has seen many a job shipped overseas. Inside the city limits, the signs of neglect and decay are ubiquitous. Clapboard houses with the paint peeling off their sides surround idle brick factories that have had their windows punched out.

Originally founded in 1785, Bourbon County derives its name from the French royal house that supported the American Revolution. There is some irony here in that the Bourbons, useful allies that they were, supported the rebels not so much because of their fondness for democracy as their rivalry with the British. Be that as it may, Bourbon County has always had its own gentry. Over the years, the Hancock family, through a combination of initiative and inheritance, has become its most prominent member.

Good times or bad, rich or poor, one thing, however, is constant in Bourbon County. Local residents are proud of Claiborne's success. When you talk to them they'll gratefully tell you that Claiborne is not only the biggest employer in the county, but also its prime showcase during the summer. In full bloom the farm consists of over three thousand acres of verdant, rolling hills broken up into neatly fenced units that vary in size from the protective one-acre paddocks where a new foal and its dam are individually kept, to the sixty-acre fields where groups of yearlings romp and graze.

At its peak Claiborne takes care of enough horses to fill up the backstretch of a racetrack, although the exact size of its horse population varies from year to year depending on the size of the foal crop, how many horses have died or been sold off, and changes in the farm's client base.

John Sosby rattled off the February 1992 figures. "Right now we're talking 24 stallions (including Damascus and Sir Ivor, who are retired), 170 yearlings, 300 mares, and we're gonna get another 200 foals before the breeding season is over. So that gives us 700 head by the first of July. Then that figure starts to drop. We'll sell some of the yearlings, both for ourselves and our clients, at the Keeneland sales in July and September. By the first of December we'll get down to 475 to 500 head when we've shipped all these yearlings that we've raised and broken to the various training centers. We've also culled some of the less-productive broodmares and the new ones haven't come in yet from off the track."

Claiborne's most important function is, of course, as a stud farm. It is one of the most prolific Thoroughbred breeding facilities in the world. During the four and a half months of the breeding season, the farm's stallions will be bred to more than a thousand mares. Even so, the pace at Claiborne remains almost bucolic. While we talked, Nijinsky II, Mr. Prospector, Danzig, Private Account, Cox's Ridge, Devil's Bag, Forty Niner, Easy Goer, and Claiborne's other stallions continued to sniff the February rain in their individual paddocks just behind the ranch-style house that serves as command headquarters. Later in the spring and summer they would spend sixteen hours a day intermittently grazing on the bluegrass and dozing in the shade.

Claiborne, of course, isn't just another Kentucky horse farm. It's an institution revered throughout the world. For nearly a century the Hancock family has not only raised great horses but helped shape the direction of the breed by the periodic infusion of new blood. The stamp of their influence is attested to by the pantheon of names that are inscribed upon the tombstones of the horse cemetery that lies just outside the main office: great imports like Sir Gallahad III (1920–49), sire of Triple Crown winner Gallant Fox (1927–58) who in turn sired Triple Crown winner Omaha; Blenheim II (1928–58), sire of Whirlaway and Mahmoud; Nasrullah (1940–59), sire of Bold Ruler (1954–71) and grandsire of Blushing Groom; and prepotent broodmare sires like Princequillo (1940–64), Double Jay (1944–72), Round Table (1954–87), Buckpasser (1963–78), Hoist the Flag (1968–80), and the inimitable Secretariat (1970–89).

Great stallions, of course, are only half the crop. Over the years Claiborne also has been home to one of the best broodmare bands in the world. Among the "Blue Hen" matrons that have foaled great horses there are Alluvial (Slew o' Gold), Busanda (Buckpasser), Con Game (Seeking the Gold), File (Forty Niner), Foreseer (Caerleon), Gambetta (Gamely), Grey Flight (What a Pleasure), Obeah (Go for Wand), Relaxing (Easy Goer), Special (Nureyev), Tuerta (Swale), Thong (Special), and the incredibly influential granddam Rough Shod II.

4

Seth Hancock, for his part, hasn't changed the farm's basic philosophy that much since he was given responsibility for running it in 1972. "The most important thing to me," he emphasized in his office one afternoon, "is still to try and raise good horses. Not only for Claiborne but also for the clients we have here like the Phippses, Henryk de Kwiatkowski, the Whitneys, Ed Cox, and so forth. Right now we have over 300 mares on the farm of which thirty we own outright and another 40 in partnership with William Haggin Perry. So the remaining 230 mares are owned by other clients, and they're as important to us as the mares we own ourselves. The best way to produce good horses is to have good stallions and good mares and then raise them right."

The Hancock family tradition of raising good horses, of course, didn't begin with Seth Hancock. It traces back four generations to Captain Richard Johnson Hancock, an Alabama native and veteran of the Civil War. He was the first Hancock to get into the horse business. Amid the vagaries of the Civil War, young Hancock joined the Ninth Louisiana Regiment and was subsequently wounded and forced to recuperate near Charlottesville, Virginia. While convalescing there he attained the rank of captain, fell in love with Thomasia Overton Harris of Ellerslie, and first entertained the idea of raising horses. During the hard years of Reconstruction, Captain Hancock first revitalized the Ellerslie estate and then slowly realized his ambition of founding a stud. By the late 1880s Captain Hancock had become a prominent Virginia breeder. He not only stood successful stallions like Preakness winner Knight of Ellerslie but also began breeding and raising yearlings for the commercial market.

His fourth and last son, Arthur Boyd Hancock, an honors student in mathematics at the University of Chicago, both surprised and delighted the good captain by offering, upon graduation in 1895, to help run the family farm, which otherwise might well have gone into eclipse. A reedy six foot six, Arthur gradually took hold of the reins and established a growing reputation for both himself and Ellerslie at the yearling sales in New York. Arthur and the captain initiated the Hancock tradition of periodically importing foreign blood to rejuvenate their stud with the purchase of the English stallion Fatherless in 1901.

The relocation of the Ellerslie stud from Virginia to Kentucky began unwittingly enough. In 1907 Arthur Hancock accepted an invitation to be a judge at the Bluegrass Fair in Lexington, Kentucky. During this fateful visit he was introduced to Nancy Tucker Clay of Marchmont, the daughter of a prominent Bourbon County family. The sparks, as they say, flew, and the following year the young couple was married. By 1909 Arthur had assumed most of the responsibility for running the Hancock stud from his aging father. And then in 1910, on the sudden death of both her parents, Nancy Clay inherited thirteen hundred acres of prime farmland. Thus Arthur Hancock now had two estates to manage, one in Virginia and the other in Kentucky. Given his love of Thoroughbreds, it wasn't long before Arthur decided to raise some horses on a portion of the Marchmont estate that had previously been devoted to corn and tobacco. The origin of how the name Claiborne came about is shrouded in hearsay and mystery. But it is a good bet that Nancy Clay's maiden name, with the spelling slightly altered, had something to do with it.

In 1913 Arthur upped the ante when he ventured to New York's Madison Square Garden and bought Celt, a speedy grandson of Domino, for $20,000 at the James R. Keene dispersal sale. Then in 1915, through the offices of the then-fledgling British Bloodstock Agency, he acquired the English stallion Wrack for $8,000. Over the next few years, as World War I approached, Arthur also bought a number of quality British broodmares at fire-sale prices. With both its stallion ranks and broodmare band thus upgraded and invigorated, the Hancock stud soon became one of the primary Thoroughbred nurseries in North America. That its yearlings could run was attested to in 1921 when Celt headed the sire list in terms of money won by his progeny.

Meanwhile, the focus of the Hancock stud increasingly shifted from Ellerslie in Virginia to Claiborne Farm in Kentucky. In 1926 Arthur Hancock saw an opportunity to further diversify his stud and formed the first major horse syndicate. He persuaded banker William Woodward, retail magnate Marshall Field, and investor Robert Fairbairn to join him in the purchase of the French stallion Sir Gallahad III for $125,000. Sir Gallahad's exotic Teddy blood, Arthur argued, might be a perfect outcross for American mares that were saturated with the domestic blood of Domino, Ben Brush, and Fair Play.

Arthur's intuition proved prophetic. From Sir Gallahad's first crop came William Woodward's 1930 Triple Crown winner Gallant Fox (out of Marguerite, a daughter of Celt) followed by his grandson, 1935 Triple Crown winner Omaha.

Having caught lightning in a bottle twice, Arthur Hancock gambled again with his outcross approach in 1936. He formed another syndicate and purchased English Derby winner Blenheim II from the Aga Khan for $250,000. Arthur hoped that the nine-year-old stallion's exotic Blandford blood would cross well with American mares. The gamble paid off when out of Blenheim's first crop came 1941 Triple Crown winner Whirlaway for fellow syndicate member Warren Wright of Calumet Farm. But perhaps an even greater testament to Hancock's judgment about Blenheim's quality is the profound influence on the breed that two of the stallion's European get would subsequently have. Blenheim's daughter Mumtaz Begum would become the dam of Nasrullah in 1940, and his son Mahmoud would become in 1947 the broodmare sire of Almahmoud, the granddam of the great Northern Dancer.

By the mid-1930s the Claiborne name had become magical and Arthur Hancock, or A. B. Hancock, Sr., as he came to be known, concluded that Kentucky was indeed the best place to raise horses. Nevertheless, it wasn't until 1946, when the Ellerslie estate was sold off, that the entire Hancock horse operation was finally consolidated at Claiborne Farm.

Meanwhile the elder Arthur prepared his son A. B. "Bull" Hancock, Jr., to inherit the Claiborne stud. Young Bull Hancock attended private prep schools in Massachusetts and Virginia but also maintained contact with the farm. During the summers his practical education included mucking stalls and alternately working with the broodmares, stallions, and yearlings as well as with the farm's noted veterinarian, Dr. Ed Caslick.

Sent off to Princeton, Bull Hancock studied French, eugenics, and genetics and played football. After graduation in 1933 he assisted his father until the outbreak of World War II, when he joined the Army Air Corps. By the time Bull came back to Claiborne in 1945, the farm was in need of revitalization. Blenheim was eighteen years old and the broodmare band had also aged. First Princequillo, with his stout Prince Rose/St. Simon–line blood, was relocated from Ellerslie in 1946 to provide an alternative to the Teddy blood of Sir Gallahad that now ran through much of Claiborne's broodmare band. Then Double Jay was also added to the stallion roster to reinfuse some of the Domino blood that had been lost over the years.

But these additions alone, in Bull Hancock's opinion, were not enough. What Claiborne really needed was a totally new outcross that would infuse more speed. To that end Bull saw the advantage of tapping into the Pharos/Nearco blood that was becoming more prominent in Europe. Following the Claiborne tradition of looking abroad, he formed a daring syndicate and secured Nasrullah, son of the undefeated champion Nearco, from Ireland for $340,000 in 1949. The rest is history. From the fiery Nasrullah came horses like William Woodward's Nashua, Horse of the Year in 1955 and broodmare sire of Gold Digger, the dam of Mr. Prospector; Red God, the sire of Blushing Groom; Never Bend, sire of grass specialist Riverman; and, of course, the inimitable Bold Ruler, who topped the sire list seven times during the 1960s while standing at Claiborne for the Phipps family. At stud, Bold Ruler's sons included Raja Baba, Boldenesian (grandsire of Seattle Slew), What a Pleasure, Bold Bidder, and the incomparable Secretariat who galloped away with the Triple Crown in 1973.

What's past is often prologue. Reflecting on Claiborne's colorful past, John Sosby leaned forward in his chair, tugged on his baseball cap, and observed, "History has proven A. B. Hancock, Sr.'s, original decision to move to Kentucky right. Kentucky is the best place to raise horses. Today we've grown to 3,481 acres and on these acres there are 44 barns with 729 stalls, and every horse at Claiborne, even the $1,000 teaser, has a stall in the winter. All our barns are built with two principles in mind, elevation and ventilation. Elevation is important because you don't want to build a barn where the water can get into it. Ventilation is desirable because it keeps the moisture out in the winter and the barns cool in the summer. A lot of these barns were originally built to cure and dry tobacco, which we still do. But they make great horse barns too."

The cold February drizzle that had greeted my arrival made me wonder about Kentucky's fabled climate as well as the horses I had seen outside. I asked Sosby about it. "Well, horsehide is tough," he reflected. "They make baseballs out of it. So horses can withstand a lot. And remember, this is our winter. The only weather I don't like to see is your cold freezing rain. Snow don't hurt horses, rain don't hurt 'em, dry weather don't hurt. We're blessed in central Kentucky with the type of weather and temperature we have. Compared to the rest of the country, it's ideal."

The farm staff had actually been expecting a more severe winter because the horses had developed thicker winter coats earlier than usual. But they had apparently been fooled by some cool fall weather. "It's a little nippy today," Sosby observed, "but it's February. We'll sometimes get a couple of days at around zero in January, and we think that's terrible. But winters have changed since I was a kid forty years ago. We used to see snow on the ground maybe sixty days a year. Now, if you total it up, we won't have two inches the whole winter. It's debatable which is the prettiest time of year here. Depends on what you want to see. There's more color in the fall, more lush green in the spring. Me, I'm a summertime man because I can find shade easier than I can find a fire."

Legally, Claiborne is a family-owned corporation in which Seth's mother, Waddell, owns 50 percent and three of her four children own the other half with Seth acting simultaneously as both president and managing partner for the group. The farm consists of three main parcels. These include the original Claiborne and Marchmont sections, along with the 684-acre Raceland parcel that Bull Hancock acquired in 1958. All the farm's broodmares, foals, and stallions are kept on the contiguous Claiborne and Marchmont parcels, while most of the yearlings are located at Raceland, several miles away on the other side of Paris. In addition, a few horses are kept at Clay Farm and at Cherry Valley Farm, which Seth Hancock privately owns and leases back to Claiborne.

Besides standing some great stallions, Claiborne has also raised some great horses. "Back in the sixties," John Sosby reminisced, "we had the Bold Rulers—horses like Queen of the Stage, Wajima, Vitriolic, and Canal. I remember Mr. [Bull] Hancock coming out with

9

some guests to Raceland shortly after he bought it and pointing out three or four Bold Rulers in each of the fields. A lot of people would live a lifetime just to have one Bold Ruler, and we'd have three or four because of our connection to Mr. Phipps. More recently we've had Ruffian, Swale, Slew o' Gold, Go for Wand, Ferdinand, and Forty Niner. We foaled and raised Easy Goer, Cadillacing, Rhythm, and Personal Ensign for Mr. Phipps. I'll never forget Personal Ensign in the Breeders' Cup in her race against Winning Colors. At the top of the stretch I thought she was beat. I turned and started to walk out. But then I saw she was comin' and comin' and at the wire she was there!"

Claiborne is unusual in this day and age in that it is run somewhat along the lines of a manor. The farm directly provides housing for many of its 149 employees, with the best homes being reserved for key personnel. This is not only a reward for loyalty and seniority, but also a management tool to allow the various foremen to react quickly to any unexpected problems. There are thirty-two employee houses on the farm plus three larger homes for the Hancock family, which includes one for Seth Hancock and his family, another for his mother Waddell, and a third for his sister Dell. Claiborne also owns another twenty-one houses in the city of Paris. Employees who don't get a house receive a monthly housing allowance of $200 in addition to their regular salary.

"Our employees range from one month of service to thirty-nine years," Sosby explained, then elaborated about his own seniority. "Right now I'm number two at thirty-five years. I can't catch that front guy, E. J. Caswell, who's in charge of the broodmare section at Marchmont. But he'll give it up someday, and I'll run him down and be the top dog."

Operationally, Claiborne is divided into two categories—the Farm and Horse divisions—with each having its own distinct uniform and responsibilities. Farm Division workers wear green uniforms and basically take care of the farm infrastructure. They normally work a forty-five-hour week and are off from noon Saturday until Monday morning. But that schedule can change if a storm or other unexpected emergency hits and there is a need for a quick cleanup or repair. Farm Division workers do everything from blacktop the thirty miles of private road that crisscross the farm, to plant trees, to repair more than a hundred miles of fencing, to mow and renovate the pastures the horses graze in. Included in the Farm Division is a battalion of carpenters, painters, electricians, welders, plumbers, and mechanics who maintain the barns and houses that Claiborne owns as well as some thirty licensed vehicles.

The vehicle inventory includes a couple of half-ton pickups, a large lowboy trailer, a backhoe, a ditch witch, and fifteen tractors that vary in size from 14 up to 105 horsepower. "The five largest tractors," Sosby explained, "pull the twenty-foot batwing mowers that manicure these fields. We mow the barn lots, the yards, and the roadways with the smaller tractors. We also have a half-mile training track that we grade. The condition of that track is very important to me for those ninety days out of the year when we're breaking our yearlings."

Maintenance by itself, of course, can't produce a good horse. A successful breeding farm needs talented horse people. That's where the men who wear the khaki uniforms of Claiborne's Horse Division come in. Many are twenty- and thirty-year veterans. They take care of the stallions, manage the reproductive cycles of the broodmares, and raise the resulting foals from the time they are conceived until they leave the farm just before they are two. Because raising horses is a twenty-four-hour-a-day process, the Horse Division is divided into two crews. The larger daytime crew puts in a forty-eight-hour week, while the smaller night section works fifty. The strain of the six-day schedule is mitigated somewhat by rotating the men's day off so that every sixth week each man can get two days off in a row.

While Claiborne expects a lot from its employees, it reciprocates with a host of benefits. Besides salary, uniforms, and a housing allowance, the farm also provides health insurance. "We have one of the best hospitalization programs of any farm in the country," Sosby elaborated. "It costs each single employee five dollars a week. If he's married with a family, it only costs him seven. Very few farms can afford to do that now. Hopefully, we can continue to do that. Each employee also gets a week's paid vacation after one year and two weeks after five years. Men that have been here twenty-five years get three weeks, unless they're a foreman in which case they get an additional week."

Claiborne also has an incentive program that encourages

employees to raise good horses. "If we win a major stakes race, the farm is always giving employees an extra week's pay. There are also bonuses twice a year, a midsummer one right after the end of the breeding season and another just before Christmas, which equals a week's work. So you can see we're different. We take care of our people because our people take care of us."

Knowing that Bourbon County is among the poorest in Kentucky, I wondered what the minimum wage on the farm was. "The minimum wage in Kentucky is $4.25 an hour and fixing to go to $4.65," Sosby responded. "But we've always been way above that. Not counting the benefits, our entry-level base salary is $235 for forty-eight hours of work. Then in thirty days they get clothes; sixty days, utilities; and ninety days, health insurance. So we do have those waiting periods. If a man has a problem, my door is always open, my Blazer has a set of brakes on it. Hey, if a man has sickness in his family, his family comes first. But don't use your family for an excuse to get off. If your little girl is sick, tell us you have to take her to the doctor at ten o'clock. No problem. Then, of course, we want you to also take care of your job."

Besides horses, Claiborne also raises burley tobacco on a share-cropping basis with some of its Farm Division workers. Burley is the primary tobacco used in the manufacture of cigarettes. "That Marlboro or Camel you're smoking may have some burley tobacco from Claiborne in it," Sosby reflected. "People don't think of us as tobacco people, just horses. But it's extra income on today's market where everybody is looking for that extra dollar. I'm a nonsmoker. We raise sixty-five acres of burley tobacco, and my daughter calls me a hypocrite. But I can live with that because the end result is an extra $100,000 for the farm and it's left up to the individual. You have that choice whether to smoke or not. Whether you want to die from smoking or drinking or racing automobiles, whatever that might be. Something's gonna take us away from here."

John Sosby is a persuasive speaker and the ultimate Claiborne partisan. Listening to him talk, one gets the distinct impression that the only thing a reasonable man can do is to fill out an application and join the Claiborne family. "I don't want to toot the horn too loud," he teased, "but the great thing is we're a team. Whatever your job here is, we all work together. Seth's the captain of the ship, but you need a lot of good sailors to make that ship go. From the man who hauls the manure away from the barn to the guy who handles the stallion, it takes every one of us to keep things going. Hopefully, all 149 of us are going in the same direction. And that direction is to have that stakes winner or have that Derby winner. If not for Claiborne, then for one of our clients. Only 20 percent of these horses are owned by Claiborne or Claiborne partners. The other 80 percent are clients. So, if Mr. Phipps or one of our other clients wins the Derby, I'm happy. If Claiborne wins it, I'm more than happy, I'm elated."

2

ORIGINS
OF THE BREED

*L*ater that afternoon, after John Sosby and most of the Claiborne staff had departed, I tossed on a rain parka and, partially to counter the effects of jet lag, ambled out along the main blacktopped road that passes between the barns where some of the broodmares are kept. Except for the occasional nickers that emanated from inside the stalls where the mares had been put up for the night, the farm was eerily quiet. Something about the silence, the falling mist, and the waning light I walked in, when juxtaposed against the horses' throaty calls, evoked a mood that was both timeless and primordial.

The Thoroughbred is a relatively modern breed of horse, little more than three hundred years old. But its evolutionary roots go back millions of years, long before there were Kentucky horse farms, English gentlemen, Bedouin sheiks, or even pictures of horses drawn on cavemen's walls. In fact, paleontologists now trace the horse all the way back to Eohippus—a four-toed, fox-size mammal that once scampered through subtropical North American forests in Wyoming, New Mexico, Colorado, and Utah some 55 million years ago.

From there the fossil evidence further indicates that, through a process of natural selection which rewarded speed and agility as well as adaptability to climatic changes, one lucky branch of the horse family that Eohippus founded gradually evolved over the next 20 million years into *Miohippus*, a larger species that stood some twenty inches at the shoulders and relied on only three toes to support its increased size and weight.

Another 10 million years of evolutionary experimentation elapsed before the arrival of the still larger and more agile *Parahippus*, an antelopelike species that subsisted on coarse savanna grass while adapting to the cooler and drier climate of the Miocene era.

It was during the late Miocene, some 5 million years ago, that *Dinohippus*, one particularly hardy descendant of *Parahippus*, followed the spring and summer grasses west out of North America and across the tundra of the Bering Straits into Asia, Europe, and Africa, thus setting the stage for the emergence of *Equus caballus*—the modern horse. This Asiatic migration, as it turned out, was crucial in that all horses subsequently became extinct on the North American continent and were not "reintroduced" until Spanish colonists brought them here in the sixteenth century.

In any event, once *Dinohippus* crossed the Bering Straits and adapted to its new environment, one particularly swift branch evolved into *Equus caballus* and began to flourish some four and a half million years ago within a vast grasslands area centered in what is modern-day Hungary. "These grasslands," according to noted paleontologist and equine scholar Dr. Deb Bennett, "extended east to the Dnestr River, north as far as the Prussian province of Holstein, west as far as the contours of the Rhone/Rhine rivers in France and Germany, and south to the base of the Alps. From there further subspecies slowly evolved as herds migrated in different directions and formed locally adapted horse populations."

Among these migrations, two branches of *Equus caballus* became particularly important as forebears of the modern Thoroughbred. One branch, which roamed west and settled along the Atlantic coast of Europe, became the "cold-blooded" Draft horse. Included in this migration and evolution were important strains of pony stock that ranged as far south as the Iberian Peninsula and extended northward throughout Brittany. Eventually, during the Ice Age some 1.5 million years ago when the sea level of the English Channel and Irish Sea was two hundred feet lower than it is today, this horse crossed over to the British Isles and Ireland.

No taller than thirteen hands (fifty-two inches) at the withers, these Draft ponies had arched necks with relatively big heads and small ears. According to Dr. Bennett, "They were barrel-chested individuals with high rumps that inclined down toward their shoulders. They were kind of built like a wheelbarrow. You can see that the modern-day quarter horse inherited a lot from these ponies. They had straight hind legs and sturdy, correct front legs with fast-twitch muscle fibers that gave them a quick turn of foot and helped them escape predators in the treeless, open terrain they populated. They further adapted to the cold grass marshland climates of the coast by evolving woolly coats and 'feathers' on their feet."

Simultaneously with the evolution of the Draft horse in Western Europe, another branch of *Equus caballus*, equally important to the future development of the Thoroughbred, migrated southeast out of the Hungarian grasslands. Some herds moved east into Georgia while others continued south, west of the Caspian Sea, into Armenia, Turkey, Syria, Arabia, Iran, and the Tigris-Euphrates Valley of Mesopotamia, near the site of modern-day Iraq. From there a small number of horses migrated west of the Nile and fanned out along the northern coast of Egypt and Morocco. Over time these "hot-blooded" horses locally evolved into the modern-day "Oriental" horse that includes the Turk, the Arab, and the North African Barb.

In contrast to the Draft ponies of the west, the Oriental horses adapted to the more arid climate and range of Africa and the Middle East by evolving angular, leggier bodies with smaller heads and bigger ears, and further "ventilated" themselves with thinner skins and shorter-haired coats. Over time the Oriental horse, which stood between fourteen and fifteen hands high, also developed the flatter musculature and narrower chest that would later be characteristic of stayers within the Thoroughbred breed.

During much of this latter phase of *Equus caballus*'s evolution, it is important to remember, human culture was still in its hunter/gatherer stage and people primarily viewed horses as food. Among the most stunning archaeological remains to be found from this early period are the Paleolithic cave paintings of Altamira in northeastern Spain which date as far back as 23,000 B.C. and include colorful paintings of horses being hunted.

Not until some six thousand years ago, around 4000 B.C., did human beings begin to domesticate and selectively breed horses. This occurred in the Dneiper River Valley, just north of the Black Sea, where tribal people were the first to develop the notion of bloodstock. Rather than depend on the uncertain bounty of the hunt, they saw the clear advantage of keeping and selectively breeding horses for both slaughter and riding.

Once domesticated, horses assumed increased military signifi-cance over the next 2,500 years. They were bred especially for that purpose by the ancient Persian shahs of the Tigris-Euphrates Valley in Mesopotamia. Archaeologists have unearthed inscribed tablets in that region that indicate Assyrian kings maintained stables of war-horses as early as 1500 B.C., and it is quite probable that the root stock of the Arabian horse as a breed originated there.

Meanwhile, in Western Europe, the coastal Draft ponies were also being gradually domesticated. Among the most skillful breeders were the Asturian herdsmen who populated the Iberian Peninsula in what would be northwestern Spain today. But it was not until around 1100 B.C. that any significant interbreeding between the western Draft pony and Oriental horses occurred.

It was the Phoenician and Lydian maritime trading culture that first brought these two separately adapted strains of *Equus caballus* back together again after a hiatus of tens of thousands of years. Shipping out from their ports in the Middle East and Asia Minor, the Phoenicians and Lydians traded between the western and eastern reaches of the Mediterranean Sea as well as all along the European Atlantic seaboard as far north as the British Isles. Besides the cattle they carried in their large open, canoelike ships, these traders also brought Oriental horses with them to their western trading outposts. Interestingly, this early horse trade appears to have flowed only one way. Whether this was the result of eastern cultural prejudice against the European Draft pony or its inability to adapt to the climate of the Levant is unknown.

What is known is that the Oriental stallions imported into the Iberian Peninsula were bred to native Draft mares by Asturian herdsmen who were quite likely the first interbreeders in Europe. The result was the Genet—a prototypical hybrid cross that would later find its counterpart in Connemara as the Irish Hobby, in Cornwall as the Welsh Pony, in England as the Palfrey, and in Scotland as the Galloway.

Oriental stallions continued to be shipped into Iberian ports throughout the Greek and Carthaginian occupations of Spain from 800 to 219 B.C. Hannibal's invasion of Rome added another dose of "hot" Oriental blood into the European equine genetic pool. With the last of the Punic Wars and the defeat of Carthage in 219 B.C., Roman culture dominated Iberia for the next five hundred years.

One of the first things the pragmatic and speed-loving Romans noticed was that the Iberian Genets were faster than any of their own Oriental racehorses. It wasn't long before Genet mares were being bred to the best Roman stallions in the hope that this new infusion of speed would produce winners in the quarter-mile races that the Romans held in their coliseums.

As the Roman legions expanded northward into Gaul and the British Isles, they brought male Oriental horses, mostly from Greece and Asia Minor, with them. A practical people, the Romans then replenished their stock by breeding their stallions to the native mares of the British Isles, which were particularly esteemed because of their more comfortable gait. "The native horses were amblers," Dr. Bennett points out, "not trotters. If you've ever ridden a horse, you know that the trot isn't nearly as comfortable a gait as the amble. Especially if you have to travel hundreds of miles. You have to remember the Romans built and maintained a vast network of roads. That's what held their empire together. Because of the needs of commerce and administration, there was a big demand for good riding horses and that meant amblers."

The Romans were also quick to notice that some of the foals bred out of native British mares had a particularly good turn of speed. These hybrids were used as couriers and the fastest became the racehorses that provided amusement for both the Romans and the natives of the British Isles.

With the decline of the Roman Empire and the onset of the Dark Ages in Europe, another important development occurred, the rise of Islam. Between A.D. 633 and 637, Muslim armies spread into the Near East and defeated the Persians. As part of the spoils of war, the victorious Bedouin sheiks incorporated some of Persia's best Oriental horses into their studs and over the next nine hundred years developed the fabled Arabian horse, which was specifically bred for its courage, refinement, and ability to run long distances in nocturnal desert raids.

Meanwhile, the Islamic Empire also established a beachhead in southwestern Europe when Berber and Arab soldiers occupied the Iberian Peninsula in A.D. 711. Over the next eight hundred years, until they were expelled from Spain by Ferdinand and Isabella in 1492, the Moors further interbred their Oriental horses with the Iberian Draft mare and Genet stock and produced riding horses, especially Coursers, that would subsequently be prized in royal courts throughout Europe.

Meanwhile, in the northern mists of Ireland, a unique breed of fleet native horses was also evolving. Gaelic poetry, according to equine historian Alexander Mackay-Smith, refers to horse racing as an important part of Irish culture as far back as 1015 B.C.—nearly a century before the advent of the Roman Empire. Over the next 2,500 years Irish warlords selectively bred the best of their largely native pony stock and produced the Hobby, a military horse prized for its swiftness and agility in the "skyrmishes" that were used to settle disputes among them.

Even the English forces that subsequently occupied much of Ireland were impressed by the superior quality of the Irish Hobbies. Records show that Henry VIII eagerly assimilated a number of them into his stud in the 1530s. In fact, Hobby speed was already well known throughout continental Europe. Bills of sale and private letters show that Irish Hobbies were imported into Italy in the fourteenth, fifteenth, and early sixteenth centuries and Hobbies were also an important component in the development of the Colonial American quarter horse.

British breeders, meanwhile, had also been busy evolving their own "Running" horses from native hybrid ponies such as the Galloway and Palfrey and, after 1530, imported Hobby strains. These "Running" horses were bred for speed and raced in sprints of up to six hundred yards that were well attended by the general populace. In addition, "Hunting" horses of mixed origin were also being bred and ridden by English nobles, who competed and wagered with one another in match races or "heats" of up to twelve miles that were run on open courses through the countryside.

It was Charles II, turf historians generally concur, who provided the impetus for creation of the Thoroughbred as a distinct breed in the seventeenth and eighteenth centuries by his establishment of the King's Plate at Newmarket in 1665. In effect, Charles II was the sport's first racing secretary. The King's Plate was a competition, consisting of three heats, for fully mature six-year-old horses that were required to carry their speed and 168 pounds over a distance of four miles.

It is worth emphasizing that, prior to the latter part of the eighteenth century, horses in England were allowed to mature before they were raced. Thus, generally they were not put into training until they were four, and they seldom competed before the age of five or six. Until the adoption of the classic English three-year-old races (the St. Leger in 1776, the Oaks in 1779, and the Derby in 1780), which were run at the shorter distances of 1¾ and 1½ miles, the 4-mile heats carrying high weights established by Charles II were the performance test British racehorses had to successfully pass before being considered worthy of stud.

Why Charles II, who was an avid horseman, should have selected the four-mile heat as the appropriate distance is an intriguing question, though it would not be surprising if the horses in his own stable best met that test. In any event, the King's Plate proved hugely popular, and succeeding kings established additional plate races in other racing centers in Britain.

With the increase in the number of Plate races, English breeders faced an interesting challenge: specifically, how to breed horses that had both speed and enough stamina to win at four miles. Their quite sensible solution was to cross the speed of the hybrid Hobby mares in their own studs with the well-known stamina of Oriental stallions, some of which were already in the British Isles.

Between 1650 and 1750 more than a hundred additional Arab, Barb, and Turkish stallions were imported into England and bred to native mares for racing purposes. The best sons and daughters from these matings were then bred back to one another and produced a distinct breed that was first legitimized with the creation of the *General Stud Book* (*GSB*) in 1791, by which time some eight hundred mares of mixed Hobby/Oriental origin were annually producing some four hundred foals.

The commissioning and publication of the *GSB* by John Weatherby was a crucial element in defining the Thoroughbred as a distinct breed. The need for some kind of registry was prompted by several considerations. While an eighteenth-century English gentleman might own a well-bred horse, apparently that didn't keep him or the person who sold it to him from occasionally either lying about or misrepresenting its origins. The preface to Volume I of the *GSB* minced no words regarding its primary purpose: "To rescue the Turf from the increasing evil of false and inaccurate Pedigrees, has long been the wish of its most noble and zealous supporters. To effect so desirable a purpose, it will be found necessary to bring together a well authenticated collection of Pedigrees, of the most noted Horses and Mares, from the earliest period."

Besides ensuring the integrity of the breed, the *GSB* had another equally important function which was: "to bring together, into one point of view, the whole Produce (as far as could be collected) of each Brood Mare of consequence; thereby reducing into a small compass, the Pedigrees of many capital Horses, and affording the Editor an opportunity of seeing what Racers of note are related to each other, and of further judging by what Stallions, the Mares bred the best Produce."

Interestingly, the fleeter hybrid stallions that resulted from the initial matings soon proved so superior on the turf to the purebred

Arab and Barb horses that after 1750 English breeders largely stopped importing Oriental stallions for stud duty. The myth of the superiority of the Oriental horse (as well as the notion that it was the exclusive progenitor of the Thoroughbred breed), however, died a slow death. In 1881, influenced by the belief that the Thoroughbred would benefit from a fresh infusion of purebred Arabian blood, a special section was introduced into Volume 14 of the *GSB* for that purpose. Initially thirty stallions and mares from the finest Arabian strains were included. After four years of special feeding and training, the best of them, a colt named Asil, was matched against the Thoroughbred Iambic in 1885. Asil was beaten by twenty lengths even though in receipt of sixty-three pounds. Considering that Iambic had previously been beaten by the great St. Simon by eight lengths when in receipt of thirty-five pounds, the disparity in performance between the two breeds seemed too large to overcome. The descendants of these Arabians as well as other imports were, however, included in the *GSB* until 1965, when numbering one hundred forty-eight they were finally deleted.

Nevertheless, the genetic contribution of the original Oriental stallions was profound. This is especially true because, in the early years, they were often bred back to their hybrid daughters in order to more quickly lengthen the distance capacities of their foals. Consequently, Oriental stallions contributed at least 50 and perhaps as high as 70 percent of the gene pool of the breed.

In any event, by the middle of the eighteenth century, through competition on the turf and selection by breeders, only three of the originally imported Oriental stallions—the Byerley Turk, the Darley Arabian, and the Godolphin Arabian—still had descendants carrying on their male line.

Of these, the Byerley Turk, a dark bay foaled about 1680, was the eldest. Trained as a war-horse, he was given to Captain Robert Byerley as part of the spoils of war after the Turks were defeated in Hungary in 1688. Following a tour of duty in Ireland, Captain Byerley subsequently retired to private life and in 1693 placed his unraced stallion in stud. Little more is known about the Byerley Turk except that he was around fifteen hands and remained in stud up to 1698, during which time he did not cover many mares.

Nevertheless, what sons the Byerley Turk got could run, and his male line continued, particularly through the great eighteenth-century bay stallion King Herod (1758). In the nineteenth century Herod's greatest descendant was probably Lexington (1850), who led the American sire list for sixteen years, fourteen of them continuously. Though Lexington did not carry on in tail male line, his female descendants appear in the pedigrees of many important twentieth-century horses, including Domino, Nearco, Mahmoud, and Nasrullah.

Meanwhile, the Herod male line was kept alive in Europe by the great French stallion Tourbillon (1928) and his best son, Djebel, to whom trace such modern horses as Ahonoora, Crozier, and Precisionist. Unfortunately, over the years it has been cursed with bad luck; some of its greatest stallions—the Tetrarch, Ahonoora, and, most recently, Precisionist—either proved infertile or died young. Consequently, the male line first established by the Byerley Turk is today in danger of extinction. Perhaps its best chance at rejuvenation lies with the aptly named Irish stallion Don't Forget Me and the Japanese-owned Dr. Devious, two of the best sons of the late Ahonoora.

Much more dominant today are descendants of the Darley Arabian, the second oldest male pillar of the breed. Standing some 14.5 hands high, he was purchased as a four-year-old bay colt in Aleppo, Syria, by Thomas Darley in 1704 and sent directly to his father in England, where he remained in the family stud until about 1730. The Darley Arabian's greatest eighteenth-century descendant was the undefeated chestnut Eclipse (1764), who inspired the famous accolade, "Eclipse first, the rest nowhere!" Eclipse, who did not race until he was six, was no less impressive at stud. In the nineteenth century his most influential descendant, both on the racetrack and in the breeding shed, was the unbeaten St. Simon (1881)—though Whalebone, Touchstone, and Stockwell also established important sire lines of their own.

In the early part of the twentieth century, Lord Derby's speedy miler Phalaris (1913) established himself as Eclipse's most influential modern descendant, especially when bred to Chaucer/St. Simon mares. In fact, the three most dominant sire lines of the latter half of the twentieth century—Bold Ruler/Nasrullah, Northern Dancer/Nearctic, and Raise a Native/Native Dancer—all stem from this Phalaris/Chaucer nick. Besides Phalaris, other important twentieth-century sire lines that descend from Eclipse include those propagated by Princequillo, Ribot, Blenheim, Hyperion, Teddy, and Domino. In fact, more than 90 percent of all the stallions at stud today carry the same Y chromosome that Eclipse inherited from the Darley Arabian some 230 years ago.

The last of the three great patriarchs of the breed, the Godolphin Arabian (1729), arrived in England a generation later than the Byerley Turk and the Darley Arabian. Apparently first known as Sham, he was a dark bay brown colt of about 14.2 hands that was noted for his stubborn temperament, black-coated progeny, and strong attachment to a particular barnyard cat. The best evidence indicates he was foaled in Yemen then exported by Syrian merchants to the stud of the Bey of Tunis. From there he was given to the King of France in 1730, who in turn sold him to Edward Coke, the keeper of St. James's Coffee House in England, who named him Sham. Upon Coke's death in 1733, Sham was bequeathed to Roger Williams, who in turn sold him to Lord Godolphin, after whom the stallion was subsequently renamed.

The Godolphin Arabian sired only ninety foals in a stud career of twenty-two years before dying in 1753. He was, according to Volume I of the *General Stud Book*, "buried in a covered passage leading to the stable with a flat stone over him without any inscription." However, what wasn't inscribed in stone was better passed on by his sons and by his granddaughter Spiletta, who was the dam of Eclipse. The Godolphin Arabian's greatest male descendant in the eighteenth century was his bay grandson Matchem (1748), to whom can be traced Australian, Hurry On, Fair Play, Discovery (the broodmare sire of both Native Dancer and Bold Ruler), and the inimitable Man o' War as well as such contemporary stallions as In Reality, Relaunch, Believe It, and Skywalker.

While the gradual evolution of the Thoroughbred as a distinct breed centered in England for the first two hundred years, an increasing number of English horses were imported into France, the United States, and South America during the nineteenth century by breeders seeking to upgrade their stock. The worldwide Thoroughbred population increased dramatically, with the estimated number of mares being annually bred rising from some 800 in 1793 to over 10,000 in 1913, to a peak of 100,000 in the 1980s.

One important result of the nineteenth-century export trade was that foreign horsemen, breeding in relative isolation, developed Thoroughbreds with distinct national characteristics of their own. In the United States, encouraged by the big purses for two-year-old races, such as the Futurity Stakes in New York, the emphasis in the latter part of the nineteenth century moved away from the four-mile heats of Lexington's time toward shorter races where precocity and speed are at a premium. In consequence, by the beginning of the twentieth century, American breeders like A. B. Hancock, Sr., gravitated toward blockier, more compact horses as best represented by the speedballs coming out of the Himyar/Domino sire lines to which more contemporary stallions like Double Jay, Dr. Fager, Ack Ack, and Broad Brush all trace.

French breeders, meanwhile, continued to breed for the stamina that was necessary to win their classic mile-and-a-half and two-mile turf races. In general, their horses were leggier, more narrow-girthed individuals as represented by such stallions as San Souci II from the St. Simon line and Dollar, Ksar, and Tourbillon from the Herod line.

Meanwhile, following World War I, English breeders began to insert more speed into their studs as best exemplified by Phalaris. On his own Phalaris, who was the fastest miler at high weights in Europe, could not outrun the limitations of his pedigree. But when his speed was matched to the stamina of the Chaucer/St. Simon mares Scapa Flow and Selene, he produced three great sons—Pharos, Sickle, and Pharamound II—that are at the very foundation of the most prized Thoroughbreds running today. From Pharos came Federico Tesio's undefeated champion Nearco (1935), who in turn sired Nasrullah, Nearctic, and Royal Charger. The temperamental and fiery Nasrullah, once brought to Claiborne by Bull Hancock, established the Bold Ruler, Never Bend, and Red God sire lines from which stem such stallions as Seattle Slew, Riverman, Mill Reef, and Blushing Groom.

Nearctic was imported (in utero) to Canada in 1953 by Canadian breeder E. P. Taylor. Though not a top-flight racehorse, Nearctic produced the great Northern Dancer (1961), who in turn sired such influential stallions as Nijinsky II, Danzig, Lyphard, Sadler's Wells, and Sovereign Dancer. Nearctic also sired Explodent, Briartic, and the underrated Icecapade, who in recent years has become more appreciated through his sons Wild Again and Clever Trick.

Perhaps the least acknowledged of Nearco's great sons is Royal Charger (1942), who produced the much-maligned Turn-to (1951), a stallion commercial breeders and trainers generally shunned because of the pedestrian looks and less than perfect conformation of his foals. Nevertheless, Turn-to's progeny have had speed, toughness, and heart. He produced Hail to Reason (1958), Sir Gaylord, and Best Turn, and their best sons—Roberto, Halo, Mr. Leader, and Habitat— have continued to have success in the breeding shed with such champions as Sunshine Forever, Sunday Silence, Devil's Bag, and Steinlen—not to mention such useful sires as Lear Fan, Lord Avie, High Brite, Bates Motel, and Cox's Ridge.

Sickle was another hugely influential son of Phalaris. While not as prolific as Pharos, his line is a reminder that, to establish a dynasty, all that is needed is one prepotent son. From Sickle's son Unbreakable came the speedy Polynesian and then the fabulous Native Dancer (1950), who won twenty-one of his twenty-two races. Native Dancer's influence on the breed, both as a sire and broodmare sire, is hard to underestimate. He is the sire of Raise a Native, who in turn sired Mr. Prospector, Alydar, and Exclusive Native, as well as the sire of Natalma, the dam of Northern Dancer. Wherever you find Northern Dancer or Raise a Native in a pedigree, you also find the blood of Native Dancer.

The third of Phalaris's great sons was Pharamound II. His male line produced Menow (1935), Tom Fool (1949), and Buckpasser (1963) as well as such top racehorses as Tim Tam, Snow Chief, and Spend a Buck. While contemporary stallions like Copelan, Buckfinder, Buck- aroo, Norcliffe, and At the Threshold have continued the Phara- mound line in tail male, its influence has been much greater on the female side. Buckpasser's daughters have been incredibly productive (especially when bred to Raise a Native–line stallions) and have established him as a paramount broodmare sire and source of stamina for the breed along with the great St. Simon–line stallion, Ribot.

It is incredible that the great Italian breeder Federico Tesio could have bred not only Nearco but also Ribot (1950) from his small lakeside farm near Dormello, Italy—in both cases relying heavily on the Phalaris/St. Simon mega nick through their respective descendants Pharos and Havresac II. An undefeated champion, Ribot won the Arc de Triomphe at three *and* four. Imported to Darby Dan Farm by John Galbreath in 1960, Ribot subsequently sired four great sons: the full brothers His Majesty and Graustark as well as Tom Rolfe and Arts and Letters. These stallions have in turn produced such horses as Pleasant Colony, Key to the Mint, Hoist the Flag, Alleged, and Lost Code. Sometimes given to savaging themselves, biting the wind, and even climbing trees, the "crazy" Ribots nevertheless are one of the few stamina influences remaining and collectively have become the most influential contemporary broodmare sires of the breed.

3

HAPPINESS IS A
HOT MARE

*T*racing the lineage of the Thoroughbred is one thing, breeding a live horse another. It was a little past seven on a Monday morning and I was with Gus Koch, who is in charge of the breeding stock at Claiborne. He was behind the wheel of one of the green-and-white Blazers the farm provides top management, and we were on our way to watch ace foreman, Billy Purcell, "tease" some barren mares in a nearby barn. Teasing, I would soon find out, is a boisterous process that involves using a surrogate stallion to help determine if a mare is "hot," or in heat.

An amiable man in his mid-forties, Gus filled me in on his background. "I'm still a new guy at Claiborne," he observed. "I've only been here fourteen years. I'm not a second-generation guy like John Sosby whose father also worked on the farm. Before Seth hired me I worked at Stoner Creek Stud, a standard-bred farm, as well as at Windfield Farm in Canada and Maryland where Northern Dancer was standing. I got some good experience that way and have seen things done some other ways. John is really deep in the Claiborne tradition. So, between the two of us you get kind of a hybrid blend and that's good. I'm in charge of the breeding stock, the mares and the stallions, and John oversees the yearlings and the farm section."

It's a the-chicken-or-the-egg kind of argument which is most important, a good stallion or a good mare. But on a breeding farm, undeniably, the most difficult job involves monitoring the reproductive cycles of the broodmares so that each mare actually ovulates within forty-eight hours of the time she is bred. Otherwise she won't conceive, and then a stallion's cover is totally wasted. When top-of-the-line stallions like Danzig, Mr. Prospector, and Nijinsky—with their $200,000 stud fees—are bred to million-dollar mares like Danseur Fabuleux (the dam of Arazi), Relaxing (the dam of Easy Goer), and undefeated Personal Ensign, the cost of a failed breeding can be considerable.

A broodmare's fertility can vary considerably from day to day, month to month, and year to year, and one of the ways Claiborne tries to bring some order to this chaos is by organizing each mare into one of three basic categories: barren, maiden, and foaling. *Barren* mares are those mares that didn't produce a foal the previous year, because they weren't bred, had trouble conceiving, or lost their foals. *Maiden* mares are those being bred for the first time. *Foaling* mares are already pregnant. In addition, all the foaling mares at Claiborne are further categorized according to their estimated time of delivery. January mares are kept in one barn, February ones in another, and so on, with March, April, May, and June mares. Organizing the pregnant mares in terms of their delivery dates not only helps the farm know where they are reproductively, but also calms them. "Keeping the same mares together," Gus explained, "helps us because they establish their pecking order and that makes the farm run easier. The more you move a broodmare around and disrupt her routine, the more chance she'll get unsettled and irregular."

In managing Claiborne's broodmare band, Gus Koch and his staff—like all modern breeders—have an important fact to contend with: namely, that mares, in their natural state, are seasonal breeders.

29

In the absence of human intervention, they will typically first come into heat in early May and then intermittently breed to a stallion until they either conceive or stop cycling in late August. What triggers a mare's ovulation is the *increased* amount of sunlight that naturally falls between those two periods. Once a mare successfully catches, or conceives, the resultant foal typically arrives some eleven months later. Normally, this will be in April or May when the grass is tall, green, and abundant and the foals will prosper—though it can be as early as March or as late as July, in which case the foals will find less forage and be correspondingly stunted. Imperfect as it is, this natural system is one that has evolved over millions of years.

Nature's reproductive schedule, however, has not suited the exigencies of the horse business or racing calendar. It is a peculiarity of racing that all Thoroughbreds, regardless of what month they are actually born in, celebrate their birthdays on January 1 of each year. In the infancy of the sport, when horses weren't raced until they were five or six, the difference between being a January or July foal in terms of performance on the racetrack was minimal. But with greater commercialization and the attendant economic pressures, horses are both sold and raced much younger today, and the difference in foaling dates can be significant. Typically, a January or February foal when sold as a yearling will be bigger and more developed than a late May or June foal and command a better price. When racing at the track as a two-year-old, the older foal will also likely have a competitive advantage. So the pressure on breeders in the horse business has been to produce earlier foals.

Spurred by the demands of the marketplace and with the help of artificial lighting, hormones, and other modern brood-mare management techniques, breeders have learned how to reprogram the estrous cycle of their mares and push the breeding season as far forward as possible. Consequently, the breeding season, not only in Kentucky, but throughout the northern hemisphere, now universally begins in mid-February. Breeders don't start earlier than February 15 because, given the normal eleven-month gestation period, they want to make sure the resulting foal is born *after* January 1. If a foal is born a week early—say on December 24—it would, according to the rules of racing, automatically become a year old on January 1, which would be a disaster because it would have to compete against much more mature horses in the same age category when it gets to the racetrack.

Because of its traditional orientation and the fact that it races most of its own horses, Claiborne is not as aggressively high tech with its mares as other, more commercial breeders. The farm does, however, employ artificial lighting as a means of getting its mares to cycle earlier. "We have two floodlights in the corners of each stall," Gus Koch explained as we drove along, "where we're artificially lengthening the hours of daylight. What we're doing is fooling these mares into thinking it's later in the spring than it really is. It's not the warmer days that makes them start cycling but the amount of sunlight. So we're increasing it a little each day the way they've done with chickens for years. With our maiden mares it's not gonna make too much difference because they just got here from the track. But our barren mares have been under artificial lights since December 1 and it works."

Not all artificial light programs are the same. Rather than using individual stalls, some breeding farms prefer to keep their mares outdoors in group pens and expose them sixteen hours a day to the same amount of light from late November until the end of May. But regardless of which approach is used, artificial lights aren't a panacea. "If we have a problem mare," Gus acknowledged, "we still have a problem mare. But it does give us an extra cycle or two on that mare. What we're trying to do is get as many mares bred as early as possible so that we get earlier foals and our stallions won't be overextended later on. We don't push too hard with our maiden and barren mares, but we're working with them."

While Claiborne has been cautious about programming its brood-mares with hormones, a lot of farms in Kentucky, Florida, and California now do so routinely. "Typically they're given Regimate for ten days," Gus said, "then put on prostaglandins. Theoretically, three or four days later they'll come into heat and be ready to be bred. Basically, programming them hastens their ovulation."

While the long-term genetic effects of programming on fertility rates is still unknown, in the short run it can create an overload in the breeding shed. "What happens is a lot of these mares ovulate and come into heat at the same time," Gus explained. "Right now our booker, Annette Couvalt, is really juggling because calls are coming in from all over central Kentucky and she has to try and book all these programmed mares to our stallions."

A couple of minutes later we pulled up in front of the broodmare barn where Billy Purcell and his assistant, Ronnie Hunt, were checking out the reproductive status of some twenty mares, most of them barren. Already halfway down one side of the shedrow, the two men were busy guiding a big squealing gray teaser in and out of several stalls to see how the mares would respond.

"Billy keeps a teasing book," Gus filled me in. "He has a page full of notes for each mare. We hope by now, since we've been teasing for almost two months, that we pretty much have a line on their reproductive cycles. The teaser Billy's handling is Ranger. He's a big draft horse and probably has a lot of Percheron in him. Later on they'll run him alongside the car and take him across the road over to the Marchmont side where we have two more barns."

The ardent action continued down the shedrow, and I watched as first Ronnie slid open each stall door and then Ranger, under Billy's tactful restraint, stuck his head in, sniffed, and approached each mare. The mares that were in heat generally *showed* their receptivity to being bred by lifting their tails, urinating, and *winking* their vulvas. Those that weren't in heat typically signaled their lack of interest in Ranger's amorous intent by trying to rip his head off with a swift kick from one of their rear hooves. Chastened, no doubt, by experience, I could see that Ranger was a teaser that had learned to anticipate a contrary response in time to duck. The errant kicks of the mares that whistled past him— *Bam. Bam. Bam.*—sounded like gunshots as their hooves hit the sides of the partially open stall doors. Surprisingly, the mares seldom injure themselves. "Once in a while they'll cap a hock or something," Gus remarked. "But not very often. They know what they're doing."

Not all farms tease the same way. While Claiborne continues the tradition of taking its teasers from stall to stall and allowing the horses to nuzzle and have some contact, most other large farms use something called a teasing board, which is actually a short outdoor wall with the mare kept on one side and the teaser on the other. Which way is better is open to debate. What the teasing boards gain in safety, they probably lose in the more precise information that comes from greater intimacy.

32

Reflecting on the teasing process at Claiborne, Gus cautioned me not to make too much over a mare's initial response. "Just because they initially kick doesn't mean they're not in heat. Nothing around here is etched in stone. They do everything. We have some mares that initially will kick. But then, when we have one of the men go into the stall and turn her around and bring Ranger in, he'll tease and then she'll start to show a little bit. It's not cut and dry at all."

Ranger's job, I could see, was a challenging one that variously required courage, ardor, and agility. To those qualities Gus added equanimity. "Thoroughbreds," he explained, "make lousy teasers. They're too excitable. A good teaser will usually have some draft horse or pony in him. Smaller horses make good teasers because they're easy to handle. They're also usually aggressive and will talk to the mares a little bit. But they're not idiots. A Thoroughbred would want to leap in the stall and be kicking at you. For teasing you need a calmer horse."

A philosophical sort, Ranger seemed to have mastered rejection and was working with both enthusiasm and equanimity. He was, as is often the case, the son of a teaser that had been bred to one of the nurse mares the farm leases to provide milk for those foals whose dams prove dry. Teasers are routinely bred to nurse mares as part of a reciprocal arrangement between breeding farms and nurse mare farms that accomplishes several objectives. First and foremost, it ensures that the nurse mare will get pregnant and continue to produce milk the following year. Second, it produces a foal. If the resulting foal is a male, the breeding farm will typically keep it and try it out as a teaser. If a female, the nurse farm will either sell her or make her into a nurse mare.

The psychological aspect of allowing a teaser to breed to a nurse mare is, in Gus's opinion, also important. "If we don't let the teaser breed to the nurse mares, then they usually lose their motivation and finally just quit on you. We gotta breed the nurse mares anyway, so when we lease her next year she's had a foal and has some milk. So the arrangement is good for the nurse mares, good for the teasers, and keeps everything going. We're fortunate our teasers are good horses. I can't overestimate how valuable a good teaser is on this farm."

Given the inherent frustrations of the job, I wondered how Claiborne went about training a horse to become a good teaser. "It just comes natural," Gus replied. "Some of them have it and some of them don't. We try out teasers that just won't tease. They'll just stand there. Then we have other ones that will go in there and attack each mare, and that doesn't work either. That scares the maiden mares to death and they won't show when that happens."

Besides agility and a calm temperament, the best teasers at Claiborne are also prized for their stamina. "A good teaser here will run up to four miles in a morning between four or five barns and tease over a hundred mares," Gus observed with admiration. "And he may have to jump four or five of them. We jump every maiden here *before* we take her to the breeding shed, so she knows what's gonna happen when we take her to the stallion. That way she's less likely to go berserk and kick the stallion. We'll let the teaser get kicked, if somebody's gonna get kicked. As the teaser jumps the maiden mares, we'll pull his penis to the side so he doesn't breed her. We let him hunch up on her a little bit and then pull him off."

Just then, a dark bay Nijinsky mare that wasn't showing pricked her ears and began backing up toward the front of the stall where Ranger was sniffing tentatively. I asked Gus what that meant. "That means she's probably gonna drive that teaser out, if he tries to come in there. These barren mares are comparatively mild. When you tease mares that have foals with them, it can get a little rough because then maternal instinct kicks in. They're trying to protect their baby too. So they don't want that teaser coming in. The teaser has the toughest job on the farm. He goes down two or three barns like this every morning and you saw the reaction he was getting, one after another. *Bam. Bam. Bam.* Then he finally finds one that's in heat and Easy Goer gets to breed her. It's tough to find a good teaser. One that handles good and then, when he does get a mare that's in heat, doesn't want to just jump in there and breed her. You want a teaser that's aggressive and will talk to the mares, yet one that Billy can control."

Picking up on some clue, Billy Purcell and Ronnie Hunt backtracked to a Spectacular Bid mare that hadn't been receptive to Ranger initially. "The first time Ranger went by," Gus explained what Billy was doing, "the mare didn't show him anything. So now he comes back and tries her a second time with Ronnie holding her and she was much better. You saw how the second time the mare stood there and raised her tail and was more receptive. They took the teaser away and thought maybe she'd *draw out*. What he's looking for is for the mare to raise her tail, urinate, and stand there, with her legs spread a little, in a breeding position, ready to be bred. But some mares will *lie* to you. They can be in heat and you can tease them four or five times and they still won't show. You may have to catch them out in the field. Some mares will only show to other mares out in the field. They're all different."

Why would a mare only show to another mare? "I don't know." Gus shrugged his shoulders. "Maybe they do it to the mares because there's not a male out there. But we can't put a male out there or they'd get bred, which we don't want. Maybe the teaser intimidates them or they feel vulnerable in the stall. For some reason some mares don't want to show to the teaser. But when she's in the field she relaxes and shows to the other mares. With some of our problem mares we'll watch what goes on out there and catch them doing it."

We moved on to a Danzig mare that Woody Stephens had trained. "Watch and see what she does now," Gus whispered. "See, her tail's up, she's winking her vulva, urinating a little bit, and backing up to the teaser. She's very receptive to Ranger. She's in heat. But she's one that's been in heat all along. Most mares will only stay in heat for seven to eight days and then go out. Theoretically, a mare will come into heat roughly every twenty days or so, but, whew, they're female so they do whatever they want to do. Especially this time of year. We've had mares that have been in heat ever since we started teasing in the middle of January. We have some mares that haven't shown at all and others that are pretty erratic. Thankfully, we had a few mares that actually have a pretty good cycle on them and we're starting to get a few bred. But even some of those, when we go to check them, our vet just doesn't feel right about and we end up passing on them and giving them a little more time. It's not easy. It's all individual, every mare is different."

Billy Purcell overheard Gus's last remark and nodded his head in agreement. A stout pony of a man with about five miles of country in him, Billy is a taciturn sort. Yet his skills don't go unappreciated by his fellow workers. As Wayne Logan, who teases the outside mares that come from other farms just before they are bred to Claiborne's stallions, put it one afternoon, "When someone like Billy Purcell on the Claiborne side or Jay Caswell over at Marchmont go to tease those mares, I couldn't do what they do. They've done it for years, working with the same mares. They'll say, 'Well, this mare right here, she don't tease good with a foal.' So they know that. And they know how to tease that mare. When they get maiden mares coming in off the track, they learn how to fool with those kind of mares too. It's an art. It takes somebody that's done it, somebody that's good at finding ways to solve the problems."

Challenging as it is, teasing is but the first step in getting a mare ready to be bred. Once a mare has shown to the teaser, the next step is to have Dr. Walter Kaufman, the farm vet, examine her with a speculum. A speculum is basically a disposable tube that is inserted into a mare's vagina which allows a vet to see, with the help of a flashlight, if her cervix is open and healthy. "If the cervix is tight and dry," Gus explained, "that stops everything right there. We make sure their cervix is open first. If it is, Doc Kaufman will then *palpate* the mare. He'll do a rectal exam where he reaches in with his arm and manually palpates each ovary to feel for a follicle, or an egg on the ovary. When he feels the follicle is ripe and soft and almost ready to ovulate, he tells Billy or me and we book the mare and get her ready to be bred."

While a number of Kentucky farms spec and palpate their barren and maiden mares every day during the breeding season, Dr. Kaufman thinks that's too much. Instead he checks each mare three times a week, on Mondays, Wednesdays, and Fridays. "On those days," Gus explained, "Doc examines all the mares that have shown or, according to Billy's notes, should have shown to the teaser. If they show follicles, he'll tell us to go ahead and breed them. The ones that haven't developed follicles yet, he'll check back on two days later. The whole purpose of the teasing and the vet exams is not to waste a stallion's cover."

Ranger, meanwhile, was now ardently courting Band, a chestnut Northern Dancer mare. She had been booked to Rahy, a speedy and precocious son of Blushing Groom that stands at Three Chimneys Farm. The booking, however, had been canceled because Band had developed a second follicle. "See, she's lifting her tail, winking, and nuzzling the teaser," Gus observed. "Band likes him. She's in great shape. Unfortunately, when Doc checked her on Saturday morning she was coming up with a second follicle, which meant there was a chance of conceiving twins, which we don't want, so we canceled it. What they're gonna do here is put buckets outside her stall and leave the lights on. So when the groom comes this morning to feed and turn out the mares, he'll know this mare stays up because we're gonna check her again. We're hoping that one of those follicles regressed or one of them ovulated and we can still get her bred this heat cycle. Otherwise, we'll have to let her go out of heat and wait until she comes back."

The prejudice against twins, I learned, isn't based on superstition, but on the fact that most mares aren't physiologically equipped to carry two healthy foals to term. What usually happens is that either one of the embryos naturally atrophies inside the mare's uterus or both embryos come to term as smaller-than-normal foals with the attendant risk of a more complicated delivery. Since breeders want to breed normal-size, healthy foals and to protect their mares, they almost universally avoid twin conception either by not breeding when two follicles are present or by having their vet manually terminate, or "pinch," one of the embryos shortly after conception.

Our attention shifted back to Ranger, who was unsuccessfully trying to engage a barren Northern Dancer mare called Swirl. She was standing stoically in the back of her stall. "What Billy and the teaser do with each mare depends upon *where* the mare is in her cycle." Gus emphasized the importance of timing. "If Billy knows that a mare just went out of heat, he'll check her real quick with the teaser and go on because he knows, unless the mare says different, that she won't be coming back in heat for another ten to fourteen days. This mare Swirl here was in foal to Gone West and was due in April, but came up empty on us. She *slipped* her foal and lost the pregnancy at some stage. She won't be going back to Gone West. Billy knows from his notes Swirl's about due to cycle again, so he's gonna check her several times. Our goal is to get Swirl in foal for 1993 to Stop the Music. He's over at Gainesway and a bit of a challenge because he's getting old and they're trying to protect his fertility by only breeding him once a day. Given what Gainesway has told us about Stop the Music, Doc will double-check Swirl and make sure she's ready to ovulate. We don't want to ship a mare to him that's not ready."

As soon as Billy and Ranger finished teasing the first group of barren mares, Gus and I hopped into his Blazer and proceeded down the smooth blacktop road to the next barn. Along the way I asked Gus about the trees that lined both sides of the road. "Well, it's February and most of these trees are still dormant, but we have some oak. On the lanes we have gum trees. They do okay, but we've lost a lot of them. We may be a little too far north for them. The big trees on the Claiborne side are sycamores. Seth's grandfather planted those and they're huge. He liked them because the horses, when they get bored, will chew the bark on a tree. But they won't bother sycamores because they have a tough bark on them. They also grow fast and give a lot of shade. We like trees. When we start young trees we put a fence around them so the horses won't injure them."

In the two days I had been at Claiborne, it had struck me as odd that I hadn't seen anybody riding a horse. "We're not a bunch of cowboys," Gus responded. "We don't have time to saddle up and roam the north forty. The only time you'll see anyone on horseback here is when we break the yearlings in October. Given the size of the farm and the need for a quick response, they're just not efficient."

Even though Claiborne remains a traditional horse farm in many ways, it has also incorporated some of the advantages of modern technology. Pointing to the two-way radio system in his Blazer, Gus said, "It's very important. This farm is so big, I'd hate to have to run it without this communication system. We have base stations in the main office, the stallion barn, the foaling barn, and the vet's office. Then we have twenty-two mobile units which include Seth, John Sosby, and myself. All our foremen and our maintenance people—which includes the fencers, carpenters, plumbers, as well as our night security man—also have a mobile unit. So everybody is tied in. Our radio system is great because it allows us to respond so much quicker to a problem."

While radio communication is important, so too are the written memos that are routed throughout the farm. "Like this afternoon," Gus illustrated, "we're gonna move eleven mares with their foals. We put out a memo two days ago, so the foremen that are gonna be getting these foals knew they were coming and the men that are gonna be losing them knew they were moving. So the barn teams would know. The van drivers also needed to know because we're gonna be vanning some of them. And the grooms are gonna walk some of them. A lot of people will be involved in this. We're also vanning some mares to the breeding shed this afternoon, so they had to know they were coming. A lot of organization goes into the farm to keep it running smooth."

Claiborne also has one foot in the computer age. Computers are used for billing and financial management as well as to punch out pedigrees and broodmare histories whenever Seth Hancock needs additional information for making a breeding decision. "All of our horse records, however, are still kept manually," Gus said. "Same thing with the health records up at the vet office. That stuff isn't entered into computers, at least not yet."

When we pulled up to the next barn, Billy Purcell was right there behind us. He grabbed a lead rope from off the barn wall, opened one of the stall doors, and brought out a new teaser, Chuck, that looked to have a lot of pony in him. Chuck was considerably more ardent and aggressive than Ranger had been. Approaching his first mare, he was neighing and dancing up a storm. Billy observed that it was Chuck's style to be demonstrative and talk to his mares.

I knew we were in the "Blue Hen" section when Gus pointed out that the mare in front of us was Relaxing, a champion older mare by Buckpasser that is owned by the Phipps family. Relaxing, of course, is the dam of not only Cadillacing but also Easy Goer, who won almost $5 million on the racetrack and now stands at Claiborne. "We checked Relaxing last week," Gus related, "and decided to give her another cycle before breeding her. She's scheduled to be bred to Mr. Prospector."

Gus's mention of the Phipps family reminded me that Claiborne has an impressive list of long-term clients. The Phipps circle includes Ogden Phipps, Ogden "Dinny" Mills Phipps, Cynthia Phipps, and Heidi Doubleday. Besides boarding mares, the family has substantial shares in Private Account and Seeking the Gold, and Ogden Phipps owns Easy Goer outright. Other prominent breeders include: Henryk de Kwiatkowski, who raced and is a shareholder in Danzig and Conquistador Cielo; Ed Cox and Martha Gerry, who raced Forego; John

Ed Anthony of Cox's Ridge, Pine Bluff, and Loblolly Stables fame; Mrs. John Hay Whitney, who formerly owned Greentree; Peter Blum; and Howard Keck, who raced and now stands Ferdinand at the farm. Most of Claiborne's major clients are involved not only as syndicate members in standing stallions but also typically board ten to twenty mares to support them.

I wondered what kind of pressure major clients like these put on the staff at Claiborne. "They're great," Gus said, explaining one of the reasons he likes working on the farm. "Our clients have confidence in us and let us do our job without a lot of petty hassles. They aren't constantly calling us up and asking 'How come my mare isn't bred yet or this yearling didn't sell?' "

We moved on to Trestle, the dam of three stakes winners, who hadn't shown anything yet. "She's by Tom Rolfe and a real producer," Gus informed me. "We've checked her three times and never did come up with anything to breed her on and now she's going out. We'll have to wait for her at least a couple of more weeks. We start early with the mares because we can't always catch them right. But we keep trying and hopefully we get them bred and in foal before the end of the spring."

Next was Kelly, a contrary, bay Secretariat mare that pinned her ears back and let Chuck know right away (*Bam. Bam. Bam.*) that she wasn't interested in him. "Kelly won over $250,000 on the racetrack," Gus told me. "She might be upset because she has a foal in another barn that's been put on a nurse mare because her milk began to dry up after only seven days. She just didn't have enough."

Undaunted by Kelly's rejection, Chuck deftly teased two more barren mares that were newcomers. They had arrived in late November and seemed fractious. "This is the first time we've had them." (*Bam. Bam. Bam.*) Gus shook his head. "So we're still learning their ways."

Watching Chuck work, a funny thought struck me. I'd bet on some horses at the track with allegedly great pedigrees that hadn't run worth a damn and wondered if a teaser had ever gotten away from the handler and covered a mare. "It's never happened here." Gus laughed. "But you always have to be careful with your teaser."

I could imagine the trouble an irate client would make if he'd paid $200,000 for Mr. Prospector and gotten the teaser instead. "No reputable breeder is gonna allow that to happen," Gus assured me. "Because a stallion's stud value depends on his getting runners and a teaser is not gonna sire any winners. And besides, they've got tests now that can confirm who the sire is."

Engrossed in his job, Chuck was now ardently pursuing Banker's Favorite, a dark bay Lyphard mare that was scheduled to be bred to Devil's Bag. She had had her first foal in 1991 but had come up barren in 1992. Banker's Favorite batted her big brown eyes once, menacingly shifted her weight, but then decided to give Chuck the silent treatment instead. Her lack of interest, Gus warned, might be just a ruse. "Now watch this." He nudged my elbow. "See, the teaser's left, but Billy is still watching the mare to see if she's been lying to the teaser and draws out after he leaves. You got to be smarter than the mare to be a good teaser."

Next Billy Purcell led Chuck toward File, the dam of Forty Niner, and one of Claiborne's most prized broodmares. As evidenced by two quick kicks that just missed, the mare was having none of him. By Tom Rolfe, a son of the great Ribot, File also comes from a strong female family. Her dam, Continue, produced five stakes winners. "File was bred yesterday morning to Private Account right before you got here," Gus informed me. "So now we're checking her to see if she's still in heat. See the way she just kicked out and reacted to Chuck. That's great because that tells us she's probably out of heat. She's ovulated and she's going out real fast. That's good. You don't like these mares that are bred to stay in and stay in and not go out of heat."

A few minutes later Dr. Walter Kaufman showed up. A heavyset, philosophical man with a high-pitched voice, Doc Kaufman has been Claiborne's resident vet for more than thirty years. He was there to palpate, or rectally examine, File and manually confirm that she had actually ovulated. After taking his jacket off and neatly folding it over the stall door, Doc Kaufman slipped his left arm into a transparent prophylactic sleeve that extended past his biceps. Next he applied some lubricant to the mare's anus and then slowly inserted his arm into her rectum, periodically pulling out chunks of fecal matter. He was cleaning the mare out so that he could reach in far enough to palpate her ovaries. Surprisingly, File didn't seem to object to this intrusion.

Doc Kaufman, who graduated from the University of Georgia's veterinary school in 1962, described the palpation process. "Usually you can tell when a mare has ovulated because rather than feeling like a large grape, the follicle on her ovary kind of collapses and you have a crater there. What happens is the egg goes down through the ovary and is released into the mare's uterus. If the follicle is still raised after a breeding, that means the mare didn't ovulate and thus hasn't conceived. So we want to see that follicle go down. When a mare's follicle has gone down after a breeding, that usually means she's caught."

Of course, when it comes to a broodmare's reproductive cycle, nothing is etched in stone. Sometimes a collapsed follicle indicates that a mare has regressed rather than ovulated. And even ovulation can be tricky. "Just because a mare has ovulated," Doc Kaufman explained, "doesn't mean she's caught. What we do with every foaling mare is to keep teasing her to see if she comes back into heat in eighteen days. Because if she hasn't caught, she should come back into heat. But some of them don't. They skip a cycle and then come back into heat. Or a mare that has caught can abort. That's why we tease every mare, even after they're bred, until the breeding season ends in June. Because a mare can do anything. You have to have a system that will accommodate as much variance as possible and still be practical. We tease our barren mares three times a week and our foaling mares every day except Sunday. This is an art, not a science, and a lot of it you do by experience. I consider follicle palpation, for example, a whole lot like playing the piano. There are a lot of people that can play the piano, but very few pianists. You've got to develop a touch."

How often broodmares are palpated varies from farm to farm and depends on the system in place. "Some farms palpate their mares every day," Doc observed. "Our approach is based on doing it every other day until they are bred. I was taught, and I still think it's good policy, to do as little as you can to the animals, because, as a general rule, that works out better than when you overdo things."

As a result of the teasing crew's skills and Doc Kaufman's deft touch, most of the mares at Claiborne are palpated only three to four times during the breeding season. Those that require extra attention are usually the ones that "lie" to the teaser in one way or another about their actual reproductive condition. Typically, these mares fall into one of two categories: mares that show to the teaser but aren't in heat; and those that don't show to the teaser but are. In either case, the only way for Doc to determine if they're ready to be bred is to see if their cervix is open and then to palpate them every other day until they develop a ripe follicle or, failing that, are given a rest.

In any event, once a Claiborne mare, like File, has returned from the breeding shed, she is routinely palpated the next day to see if her follicle has collapsed. In File's case, Doc was pleased to say that it looked like the mare had caught. "Assuming she doesn't come back into heat and show to the teaser," he added, "we'll ultrasound her in about eighteen days to confirm she's in foal and to make sure she hasn't twinned." Removing the used sleeve from his left arm and putting on a fresh one, Doc Kaufman moved on to Narrate, an Honest Pleasure mare, who was "red hot," according to the teaser. This was the third time Doc was checking her, but he still didn't feel much of a follicle. He decided to give the bay mare another two days and palpate her again on Wednesday. Hopefully, by Friday her follicle would be ripe and she would be ready to be bred.

Besides being a legendary vet in central Kentucky, Doc Kaufman is also a successful breeder and racer of his own horses. The combination intrigued me, and I asked him about it. "You know, I've worked with the best horses in the world and some of the best people," he reflected. "But I don't think you can understand this business unless you breed or own a racehorse and pay the bills associated with it. Yet it's so much fun. What this business is basically doing is selling one thing, and that's *hope*. That's the real bottom line. You have a mare and you hope she's decent. You hope she gets in foal. You hope the foal's okay and you hope it can run. You can breed to a Mr. Prospector or a $5,000 horse, but the bottom line is you're hoping to breed a good horse. That's what you're in this thing for. If I beat a good horse, that means I have a better one. The most fun in this business is planning a mating, getting a foal, watching it develop, and then watching it at the racetrack. You really get hooked up when you get your two-year-olds to the racetrack."

Doc Kaufman has a puckish sense of humor that came out when he talked about his best runner, a filly named No Choice that won over $392,000. "She was by Navajo, a son of Grey Dawn II, and out of a mare called Submission that my partner Dr. Webb claimed off the racetrack. Anyhow, I bred Submission to the cheapest stud we had here, Navajo, and came up with the name No Choice. I figured if her daddy was a Navajo and her dam was named Submission, then the foal had to be called No Choice."

No Choice's prospects seemed initially bleak. "When the yearlings would run in the field she was always dead last." Kaufman continued his tale. "We didn't nominate her to the Breeders' Cup because of that. I thought maybe I should have named her No Chance. But, when she went to the racetrack, she was the best by far. One of the great thrills in my life was when she won the Gardenia, which is a $150,000 stakes race. She only won by a nose, but she won. I was so excited I could hardly remember my name or anything else. She was the kind of horse, like Forty Niner, that would put her ears back and dig in at crunch time. When Seth let me foal-share her with Forty Niner, that was a great compliment to the mare. I'm hoping that he gets rewarded for it. I told Seth at the time that it would be interesting to see if the *try* in both of our horses gets transmitted to the foals. I talked to Steve Penrod, who has our colt now, the other day and told him this story and he said, 'I don't think you have to worry about that. We had to stop working the colt in company because he gets too damn competitive.' The colt's name is Tackle. I don't know how he'll do, but having a young horse like that really gives you something to look forward to. I also have another mare that's in foal to Conquistador Cielo."

Doc Kaufman emphasized it's the intangibles that keep him in the game. "Everybody wants to reduce this business to dollars and cents and it won't work. If you take a dollar-and-cents approach to this business, you'd get out. When you breed a good horse and it wins a stakes, that's what's great about it. Plus it gives you bragging rights! It's like hitting a hundred-to-one shot. Most people now want to analyze everything. But if you analyze everything, you lose that sparkle in your eye. You lose that hope. Horse racing is like listening to a great aria in an opera. It affects people in different ways. But what it does for you is beyond price."

Given Doc Kaufman's veterinary and breeding experience, I wondered what he thought about various breeding theories. I started off by asking him about inbreeding. "Years ago I had a friend named Bishop." Doc paused for effect with a twinkle in his eye. "And he liked to speculate about what would happen if you bred Secretariat to one of his daughters. At the time I thought, Why in the world would you want to do that? Well, years later, I ended up with a Secretariat mare and got to thinking about it. See, Secretariat seldom stamped his offspring. Most of his offspring looked like their dams. So, I wondered what would happen if I bred a son of Secretariat to one of his daughters. So I did that. I bred Executive Order to Ravel and named the ensuing foal Bishop's Idea. She's four now and has won four races and $63,000. [Bishop's Idea subsequently won three stakes and increased her earnings to $153,000.] Probably nobody else would do a thing like that, but it worked. I tried it again, but the second foal couldn't stand training. It'll be interesting to see how Bishop's Idea does as a broodmare. She not only has a double dose of Secretariat, but a triple dose of his dam, Somethingroyal."

The Thoroughbred, like all breeds, is, of course, already the product of significant inbreeding. Computer studies by geneticist Patrick Cunningham have shown that 80 percent of the current gene pool of the breed traces back to some fourteen stallions and eleven mares—with the Godolphin Arabian (14.6 percent) and Old Bald Peg (3.1 percent) respectively being the largest male and female contributors. So every time two Thoroughbreds are mated, breeders are, willy-nilly, randomly doubling up on a tremendous number of common genes. Arguments about inbreeding, therefore, are really ones of degree. While close duplication of a prepotent ancestor within the first four or five generations of a pedigree may increase the probability of getting a superior racehorse, on the down side there is also the increased risk that recessive and previously hidden genes will become dominant and pass on negative and even lethal traits.

Within the breeding industry, Leon Rasmussen, the former bloodlines analyst for the *Daily Racing Form*, and Jack Werk, publisher of *Owner/Breeder* magazine, are strong advocates of selective inbreeding to superior individuals. Analyzing the four-generation pedigrees of all the Eclipse Award winners, Werk points out they are some 28 percent more inbred than the general horse population. This statistical fact, in his opinion, strongly suggests that selective inbreeding increases the probability of getting a superior horse.

Pedigree researcher David Dink, on the other hand, in a series of articles published in *Thoroughbred Times*, has questioned the merits of inbreeding. Based on his survey of the entire foal crop of 1983, he concluded that the percentage of stakes winners that were inbred was not significantly greater than those that were not inbred. Dink argues that if inbreeding really works, it has to apply to the whole population, not just a select few. Interestingly, Dink's study tentatively indicated that, if one is determined to inbreed, it makes a significant difference within which generations an ancestor is duplicated. On average, inbreeding within the second and third generations produced a significantly lower incidence of stakes winners than inbreeding within the fourth and fifth generations. And even better results were produced when superior male ancestors in the sire's family (particularly Bull Lea, Mahmoud, Nearco, Polynesian, Hyperion, and Nasrullah) were duplicated in the dam's female family.

Statistical studies of horses, of course, are finally just that. They are based on averages and probabilities and not absolute truths. Each breeding is a unique, nonreproducible event. Because racing performance is a complex trait that involves not only genetics but also environmental factors such as nutrition, training, and even racing luck, quantitative studies can never be conclusive. The fact is that when it comes to planning a specific mating, even the best breeders fail 85 percent of the time and there will always be room for the curious and the intuitive to play, and that may be one of the principal allurements of the game.

For romantics there is even the seductive story of how Signorinetta, who won both the English Derby and Oaks, was bred in the spring of 1904. It seems that her dam, the top race mare Signorina, had been retired in 1892 and for the next twelve years was bred to the best stallions in England without producing even one outstanding foal. Then, when she was seventeen, her still-undaunted owner, the Neopolitan gentleman Cavaliere Ginistrelli, arranged for Signorina to be bred to one of the great stallions of the day, Isinglass, for the then considerable sum of 300 guineas. On the appointed day, however, as

Signorina was being led across town through the streets of Newmarket to her appointed tryst, she encountered the common stallion Chaleureux, who, after savoring her scent, became so infatuated that he broke out into a chorus of whinnies and neighs and refused to move. Persuaded by his charms, Signorina whinnied back and despite her groom's goading, also refused to budge, whereupon an amused crowd began to collect. An inspired Ginistrelli sized up the situation and decided that since all else had failed, maybe the horses knew something. He declared, "They love! A love match it shall be!" Though the mating was scorned by all the experts, who considered Ginistrelli out of his mind, eleven months later the "love child" Signorinetta was foaled and went on to win first the Derby and then two days later the Oaks.

In any event, some eighty years later Doc Kaufman had indulged his fancy, gambled on inbreeding with Bishop's Idea, and beat the odds. I wondered what he thought about Dosage, another controversial approach to breeding first developed by the retired French cavalry officer Colonel J. J. Vuilliers, who was a highly successful pedigree consultant for the Aga Khan at the turn of the century. Predicated on the assumption that only a few superior horses influenced the development of the breed, Vuilliers identified sixteen nineteenth-century horses, including the mare Pocahontas, and acknowledged their prepotent influence by designating them as *chefs-de-race*. From there Vuilliers developed an outcross system for mating a stallion to a mare that was based on a sixteen-generation study of their pedigrees. Vuilliers calculated the percentage of "blood" contributed by each *chef-de-race* and especially looked for significant differences (*écarts*) in the amount of St. Simon blood in the two horses. Vuilliers believed the greater the difference, the more likely hybrid vigor would result and produce a superior horse.

After Vuilliers's death, his Dosage system was modified and transformed by the Italian scholar Franco Varola. Varola expanded the list of *chefs-de-race* in the 1970s to bring it up to date, while simultaneously categorizing each horse into one or more of five aptitudinal tendencies—Brilliant, Intermediate, Classic, Solid, and Professional. While, at the extreme ends, Brilliant *chefs* imparted great speed to their progeny and Professional ones passed on stamina, Varola's typology also tried to accurately "fix" a horse's temperament, body type, and "moral" qualities.

In the 1980s, geologist turned pedigree consultant Dr. Steven Roman further modified the Dosage system. He developed a five-generation mathematical expression of the aptitudinal tendencies of all the *chefs-de-race* in a pedigree as a means of predicting the distance capacity that would likely result from a specific mating. Leon Rasmussen then popularized Roman's approach in the *Daily Racing Form* as a handicapping tool for predicting the Kentucky Derby winner, though not without subsequent misgivings.

While Roman's approach, particularly his designation of *chefs-de-race*, has come under severe criticism in recent years, Dosage continues to evolve in the hands of other advocates. On a practical level, Ken Carson, the pedigree analyst at Three Chimneys Farm, incorporates it, much as Vuilliers originally did, as one tool in his mating recommendations. On a more theoretical level, veterinarian Dan Lochner has recently contributed to Dosage's further refinement with his book *Modern Dosage Theory*.

Drawing on his practical breeding experience, Doc Kaufman was extremely skeptical about Dosage's benefits. "I don't think it's worth a damn." He pulled no punches. "I say that because Nasrullah was bred to Miss Disco seven times and got six different foals. They all had the same exact Dosage and yet ran totally different. Now, you can account for the good ones with Dosage, but you gotta account for the bad ones too. How do you do that? I don't understand how because you've got 500 million sperm. I'd go along with Dosage if you had one sperm and one egg. But you've got millions of sperm. Just think of the odds of a good one hitting that damn egg. Of course, that's why Mr. Prospector has a stud fee of $200,000. He's got more good sperm than most. But the big thing in breeding is still luck. You gotta get the right one."

Doc Kaufman elaborated as to why he feels skeptical toward most breeding theories. "I was down at the breeding shed for years and years and I watched good mares and bad mares and indifferent mares, and there was no common denominator as to who had a good horse. Some of the best broodmares in the world looked like hell. There's no answer to it. Nobody can corner it. That's the best part of it. The best thing about luck is that no matter how much money you have, you can't buy it. I know a woman who picked a mare that was unraced and bred her to a horse that was unraced, and she came up with a stakes winner. You see, that's what keeps a lot of us in business. That hope that we can get lucky and get a good horse."

No doubt, but the odds definitely seem stacked in favor of a farm like Claiborne because it has so many more good horses to breed from. "Sure they are," Kaufman acknowledged. "But Claiborne doesn't keep the horse business going. It keeps the upper part going, but the bottom part is the ballast that keeps most breeders going. The claiming horses put on a bigger show than the allowance and stakes horses. So there's room for everybody in this game. Whatever theory you got, there's something about horses that will prove you wrong."

Doc Kaufman elaborated on the vagaries of his own breeding experience. "I had a mare and I bred her to a horse we had here named Tell who was a son of Round Table. I got a short-coupled, stocky colt that I sold which ended up winning about $89,000. So then I bred the same mare to Tell again the next year. And I got a long-bodied, long-headed, big filly, and she won $129,000 in New York. Same parents, but entirely different body types. So I took the mare again and bred her three times to Le Fabuleux. I got a small filly and big filly. Both of those were bays. And then the last one I got was a nice big chestnut colt. All different types from the same stallion and the same mare. Of course, you see that in people too. But that makes me wonder about the guys that measure and do all this stuff. I didn't get the same thing. They weren't even close. So I don't see how in the hell all these guidelines people promote really work."

What then about the favorite resort of the desperate breeder looking for order in the universe, the idea of a nick, the matching up of complementary bloodlines? "Well, Nasrullah/Princequillo was a nick. It had to be. I'll tell you another nick that I think is an absolute perfect nick; look at Rough Shod II. She was bred to Nantallah four times and got Moccasin, Thong, Lt. Stevens, and Ridan. Now, that to me is a perfect nick. Out of that nick came horses like Nureyev and Alysheba.

That had to be a super nick. Mr. Hancock, if I remember right, bred her back to Nantallah before he knew it was gonna work. So this is an intuitive business."

I wondered what Doc Kaufman thought about those horses that are world-beaters on the racetrack but never contribute anything else to the breed. "Those are what I call freak horses," he replied. "Carry Back was a freak. He was a great racehorse but that was it. Snow Chief is maybe another. John Henry was a gelding so we didn't have a chance to find out if he could have contributed. Ole Bob Bowers had that one good sperm and who knows if it would have carried on."

Before we could pursue our conversation any further, a barn hand came up and informed Doc that an urgent message had come over the radio from Raceland regarding a Mr. Prospector yearling colt that was experiencing colic. Excusing himself, Doc grabbed his coat, hopped into his truck, and was gone. With that kind of breeding, he didn't have to tell me, you don't fool around.

Ten minutes later Gus Koch and I jumped back into his Blazer and headed for the main office. Along the way we talked about the daily routine of the broodmares at Claiborne, which varies depending on their condition and the season. In the winter months, beginning on the first of December, all the mares are brought in from the fields by three in the afternoon, put in their various stalls by categories, and fed. In preparation for the breeding season, the barren and maiden mares are put up for the night under artificial lights while the already pregnant foaling mares are kept in unlit stalls. The next morning when the day crew comes in at seven, all the mares are fed again and then turned out for the day.

The only variation in this winter routine is that starting early January, the barren and maiden mares are kept in barns a little longer three mornings a week so they can be teased and their heat cycles recorded for the beginning of breeding season on February 15.

By the second week of April both the weather and the routine change, and the mares are kept outside most of the time. "We usually have enough grass around here," Gus explained, "and the weather straightens out enough then that we can take all the maiden and barren mares, which is probably about 120 head, and turn them out and leave them out for the next six months. The only thing we do is bring them in three times a week and tease them because we're still breeding them until the first of July. By the first of June most of the barren and maiden mares have been bred and a lot of them are in foal. The weather's fine, there's plenty of grass, and they don't need to be in the barn at all."

The same routine basically holds for the 200 mares with foals by their sides that have been rebred, except they aren't turned out full time until May and even then they are still brought back in every morning for a few hours so they can be teased and given supplementary feed.

Not surprisingly, because of the large number of mares involved, the feeding program at Claiborne is standardized. In the winter the farm generally gives one cup (two quarts) of feed to its mares in the morning and two cups in the afternoon. Claiborne's basic feed is a 14 percent mixed protein formula that consists of 60 percent oats, 20 percent cracked corn, 10 percent bran, 10 percent soybean pellet, trace mineral salts, and a 7 percent molasses glue that ties it all together.

"We basically use the same feed all over the farm," Gus noted. "The only difference is sometimes we'll change the size of the portion depending on what's happening with a horse. The mares that have foaled already are getting two cups in the morning and two in the afternoon because they've got to produce that extra milk for the foal. Some of the maiden mares that are just off the track are a little light and we feed them a little extra too. With stallions sometimes we have to cut them back because they can get too fat."

Claiborne's mares also get plenty of roughage. In the winter, besides their sweet feed, they get all the hay they can eat, which comes to more than 40,000 bales a year. "Right now," Gus estimated, "we probably split a bale of hay a day in this barn to about every three barren mares. Our main source of feed is normally in our pasture, but in the winter there's not much there. Some breeders tend to be neglectful of their winter nutrition when it comes to barren and maiden mares, but that's a bad policy. We feed them lots of hay until early April, when they'll be out twenty-four hours a day eating that lush Kentucky bluegrass. They're better off on that than they are in here eating hay that's a year old. And we'll keep them out there until December, when the schedule reverses and we bring all the mares in at night and put the barren and maiden mares under lights again to get them ready for the breeding season."

4

STUD TALK

A little before eight the next morning I met up with John Sosby and Gus Koch at the same breeding shed where Sir Gallahad, Blenheim, Nasrullah, and Bold Ruler had once performed their duties. A half-dozen vans were already parked in front, and their drivers were unloading the red-hot mares that had been shipped in from surrounding farms. Over the next hour they would be bred to the likes of Mr. Prospector, Danzig, Private Account, and Nijinsky as well as promising but unproven stallions like Forty Niner, Proper Reality, and Seeking the Gold.

"You can see that our breedin' shed is nothing fancy," John reflected about the single-story wooden building in front of us. "But that's okay. Why spend a million dollars for something you don't need? Especially when what worked for Nasrullah and Bold Ruler still works for Mr. Prospector and Danzig."

Built in 1905, the breeding shed is functionally divided into two separately enclosed areas. The front section, closest to where the incoming vans are parked, is where every outside mare is first reteased to make sure she is still in heat and receptive to being bred. As always, the farm's primary concern is to avoid wasting a valuable cover on an unfertile mare as well as to minimize the risk of injury to the stallion from an obviously contrary one. Once the mare passes muster, her tail is wrapped, then she is washed and walked to the back of the building. From there she is quickly led in through the fifteen-foot opening into the padded thirty-by-thirty-foot breeding area where she will soon be joined by the stallion.

While some 50 percent of all fillies become broodmares, it is a hard fact of Thoroughbred life that only 5 percent of the colts go to stud, and of those less than one in ten prove successful. Interestingly, these percentages aren't too different from what you find in a state of nature where, typically, a dozen or so mares are presided over by a stallion who has prevailed over his competition. Even though the question of which colts get to breed on is now decided by performance on the racetrack, that hasn't changed their essential nature. "All stallions," John emphasized, "have to be kept apart. Even if there's no mare around, they'll fight. It's the nature of the creature that they'll fight until the death of one. Mares and yearlings will not do that. But a stallion will."

While the broodmares, foals, and yearlings are important, John Sosby believes that the stallions are the key to Claiborne's success. "To me they are the most important part of the wheel. Those stallions have got to produce. Our breeding rights and our fees and things that allow us to run this farm all depend upon the success of our stallions. So they have got to succeed. From there you go to your broodmares that will produce that good horse and on to the yearling operation."

Training a colt to run big at the racetrack is one thing. Successfully managing a stallion in the relative isolation of a stud farm is another. I'd seen the air-brushed photos and progeny statistics in the stallion registers, but now was about to experience the real thing. Turning toward John, I asked him what happens when a stallion first comes to the farm.

"Well, that's usually in the early fall," he replied. "And, hopefully, we can turn him out into his paddock that same day. First thing we do is take those racetrack shoes off him and, as long as he's at Claiborne, he'll never carry weight on his back again. Next, Doc Kaufman will probably tranquilize him so he doesn't get too excited. And then we'll lead him into that two-acre paddock where we'll have maybe thirty men strategically placed inside the perimeter of the fence and around the water tank. Then the head stallion man will lead him to the center of the paddock and then walk him around the paddock once before bringing him back to the middle and turning him loose. From there some of them will start to graze, while others might run just a little. Meanwhile, we've kept those thirty men around the perimeter to keep the horse from getting excited and running into the fence. But we haven't had any bad problems with our new stallions in years because they're coming from good people who know how to treat a horse."

As soon as a new stallion has acclimated to life on the farm, he is test bred to one of the nurse mares that is in heat in order to educate him to the routine of the breeding shed. "You need to get him used to how to mount a mare before the breeding season begins," John explained. "They're all virgins when we get them. Some of them take to it like a duck to water and others have to learn. I've seen some stallions fall off, others get both front feet on the wrong side from the rest of their body, and still others get right into the groove from the start. I've also stood there for an hour and seen sweat run off of them. They just couldn't get up on the mare."

So what does Claiborne do when a multimillion-dollar stallion prospect has a severe case of performance anxiety, perhaps because he has been too severely dissuaded from showing interest in mares during his racing career? "You don't abuse him," John Sosby cautioned. "He'll get up. Nature has a way of making things happen. We've stood there, I think, where we were more worried than the horse was. Yet we knew he would eventually get up, because we've never seen one that wouldn't. Usually they get the hang of it after a mare or two, though sometimes it takes three or four. We've never had to reject a stallion because he wouldn't cover his mares, but we've had to reject some that would. They're not all gonna be a Secretariat, Mr. Prospector, or Danzig."

Sosby's last comment was a reminder that breeding, like racing, is a

tough game. Not only the broodmares but also the stallions are constantly culled. As good a racehorse as Spectacular Bid and Track
Barron once were, for example, they couldn't compete against Kentucky's best stallions, and Seth Hancock had to ship them off to New
York and Oklahoma, where they could attract a larger book of less
expensive mares. The harsh truth is that even the best stallions can go
years without siring a Classic winner, and most of them are lucky to
average 10 percent stakes winners to named foals. While stallions like
Nureyev (21 percent), Danzig (20 percent), Nijinsky II (19 percent),
Mr. Prospector (17 percent), Pleasant Colony (16 percent), Riverman
(14 percent), Silver Hawk (13 percent), and Seattle Slew (13 percent)
are at the top of the stakes-producing pyramid, the industry average is
under 3 percent, with many stallions never siring even one Graded
Stakes winner. And producing Graded Stakes winners is important
because, if you want to hit a home run in the racing game, that's where
the money is.

For the average owner/breeder/yearling buyer, who keeps the
industry going, the odds of success are considerably longer. Most of
their horses are lucky to win even at the claiming level, and only 5
percent of all runners annually pay their way. "Only a third of the
horses that are born ever win a race," John Sosby acknowledged, then
elaborated on his own experience. "I have a four-year-old filly that I
bred. Two years and $35,000 later, we finally win a Maiden Claiming
race at Turfway, last Friday night. And luck is important. I mean good
luck. Sometimes even without the knowledge of what you're doing,
you can get by, if you have good luck. The other way around, bad luck,
you don't need. Swale was good luck that turned into bad luck for
Claiborne. That dream that the Hancocks chased all their life, and all
my life, to win the Kentucky Derby and suddenly you're there! It
happens! To me it was like a dream. Golly, it happens and then you
lose it. Swale was going to come back here to stud. We were going to
put him in Bold Ruler's old stall. Then he died right after winning the
Belmont. We wanted to stop the day they put him in the ground. What
the hell. The dream is gone. But you reach down and get that boot-
strap because you know if you can hang on to that wheel long enough,
your slot's gonna come again. And then, when you see that foal in the
field, it starts again. Not as an owner, but as a manager. As an owner I

dream that American dream that I'm gonna catch that lightnin' in a bottle. I know it happens. Could it be me?"

That same hope drives most handicappers. Though they tapped out today, tomorrow is a new day. "It's a good thing horses *don't* run true to form," Sosby reflected. "If they did, the most logical gamblers would corner the market. That's what makes horse racing interesting. Horses come in all sizes, shapes, and colors. He might be black, gray, chestnut, big or small. He might have no pedigree or a lot of pedigree. So, who's gonna win? Give me luck, Mike. I'd rather be lucky than good."

For John Sosby, luck also dominates in the breeding shed. Every time a stallion covers a mare, it's a genetic crapshoot that determines which one out of millions of sperm will actually impregnate the egg and how those genes will mix. "Just like where lightning will strike." John marveled at the mystery. "I have no control. So I got to ride it out, what Mother Nature gives me. Hopefully, she's nice to me and gives me a stakes winner. But Mother Nature can be cruel sometimes like in that foalin' barn."

Fortunately, optimism reigns supreme in the breeding shed, and once the breeding season gets into high gear, Claiborne's stallions are normally bred twice a day: once between eight and nine in the morning and again between three and four in the afternoon. The morning shift is generally busier, with up to fourteen mares being bred, while the afternoon session rarely exceeds eight. By comparison, nearby Gaines- way, which is a more commercially oriented farm, stands twice as many stallions. In order to accommodate its clients, it maintains a double breeding shed and runs three shifts a day: one at nine in the morning, another at two in the afternoon, and the last at seven in the evening.

The mares, of course, don't just show up randomly to be bred. Each mare must first be *approved* by whoever controls the season to the stallion. With a Claiborne-owned stallion like Forty Niner, Seth Hancock has total authority to approve which mares go to him. With syndicated stallions, each shareholder, or the individual who has bought a season from the shareholder, decides. In either case, it remains one of Seth Hancock's most important responsibilities to recommend those mares that will give each stallion the greatest possi- bility of success and thus enhance his value at stud.

Once a mare has been approved, the next step is to book her to the stallion. At Claiborne the tricky responsibility of scheduling more than a thousand mares to their designated stallions is handled by Annette Couvalt, a former employee of the *Thoroughbred Record*. Given the fickle nature of each mare's heat cycle, Annette's job is far from an easy one. "Annette really runs this place during the breeding season," John Sosby remarked only half kiddingly. "People think she just answers the phone. But basically, she organizes everything and we just do what she tells us."

John's description of Annette's job intrigued me enough that I looked her up a couple of afternoons later. After all, I reasoned, you can't breed a stallion if the mare isn't there. An articulate woman in her mid-thirties, Annette made an observation that echoed what Gus Koch had told me previously. "I've never been so busy this early in the breeding season. A lot more people have been programming their mares with hormones trying to get earlier foals, and they're inundating our stallions. Right now our stallions are so busy that I'm missing mares. There are mares ovulating without being bred because the workload of the stallions is so heavy we can't get all the mares in."

The mid-February influx of programmed mares troubled Annette because traditionally Claiborne has believed in easing its stallions back into the routine of daily breeding. "Last week," she spoke with alarm, "we had the dilemma of having way more stallions booked than we wanted to breed. Because, especially with the older horses, we like to let them build up their stamina a little bit. You don't want to hit a twenty-two-year-old stallion like Mr. Prospector with two mares his first day out. You want to do one mare a day for several days. After three or four successful covers, when he knows we're back to breeding and we've gotten him conditioned toward breeding again, then we'll breed him to two mares that day. From there we'll pick up speed to where he's covering two mares every day. With older horses like Nijinsky and Mr. Prospector, you can't just overload them with mares because you're just asking for trouble."

A Claiborne veteran of fourteen years, Annette books all the outside mares on a first-come, first-served basis. Many of the mares are shipped in from local boarding farms in Midway and Versailles, which are only about a forty-five-minute van ride away. "But I don't just fill in the spots," she emphasized. "I'm not gonna overbook. For Nijinsky I have two mares right now that want him, but we don't want to overextend him. So, often the timing isn't right."

So how does Annette, who works from six-thirty to five, seven days a week, during the breeding season, handle the overload? Does she tell clients to check back in two weeks?

"Well, I've never put anybody off two weeks." She laughed. "But I've had to book a week later than they wanted. After a certain point in the breeding season, I just start stringing them out in a row because I have to leave myself some working room to juggle mares back and forth. I not only put them on the book when they call, but a lot of the mares move once or twice before they get bred."

Typically, an outside breeder will call Annette up and say a mare is in heat and want to book her. "Say it's a Sunday." Annette gave an example. "They could book her for a Tuesday or Wednesday or even tell me, 'I got to go today.' But the mares don't get to read that book that says they oughta be in heat a couple of days, produce a good follicle, then get bred and ovulate and go right out of heat. That's the perfect textbook mare. But a lot of times a mare will come right up to where you think she's going to ovulate that day—you think she's gonna be lucky if she lasts till three o'clock to get to the breeding shed. Then the next day she's still in heat and they palpate her and that follicle on her ovary has regressed. It's actually gotten smaller and harder again. Or maybe the mare's coming up with another follicle and now there is the possibility of twins. So they cancel. There's a bunch of different things that can and do happen. I'm just the paper person here, but believe me, I hear every sob story there is. I don't think there's anything a mare could do that I haven't heard about. On the other hand, a lot of mares do exactly as they're supposed to. I mean, they're bred right on the money and go out of heat. But then they don't get in foal. They might do that all spring long and you still won't know why they didn't get in foal."

The fact that mares periodically go barren interested me. I wondered if mares, like soil, sometimes need to lay fallow, to be given a year off. "That seldom happens here," Annette responded. "We prefer to breed them back until they tell us to stop. In Europe they call it *resting* a mare. Over the last couple of years because the horse business has turned down so much and people either have less money or are afraid they aren't going to have the money to pay stud fees, I have had the feeling that a lot of mares who foaled reasonably early, say April or May, and could have got two or three shots to be bred and had another foal, some of those people have said, 'Well, she's a little late, we're gonna give her a year off and breed her back earlier next year.' But, at the lower echelons, I think what they're really saying is they want to give their pocketbooks a year off too. They have an empty mare. She's not earning any money for them. But she's not costing them a stud fee either."

The best broodmares, interestingly, are seldom rested. "If you have a mare that's extremely valuable," Annette observed, "you're not going to do that. Because she's not going to last forever. She can only have one foal a year, so you better use her. A typical maiden mare will come here between the ages of three and five. She may well be producing until she's twenty years old. She might have fifteen foals. If she has that many, she gets a blue ribbon. We don't take a mare like that out of production."

Typically it's a younger mare who has been foaling late that is rested for a year. "In that case," Annette explained the strategy, "an owner may not want to keep that mare always foaling late. So he'll bite the bullet and skip a season so the mare can start out early the next one and have an earlier foal the following year. Typically she didn't come in early off the track her first year and she's always gonna be late unless she skips a year. If it's an older mare you seldom skip a year, because you don't know how much longer she's gonna be productive."

Nevertheless, some older mares are taken out of production. "If a mare has some physical problems, if she's sick, we don't force things on her that she's not physically ready to handle. There are mares that Seth has retired because physically they're not aging gracefully. But we don't rest them, just to give them a year off. It doesn't seem to be a very feminist thing to say, but pregnancy doesn't seem to be that hard on the mares. When they get in foal, the foreman will often say he thinks a particular mare is in foal because her coat has really taken on a special sheen and dappled out—just like the horses naturally do later on in spring when the grass gets better and they feel better. A pregnant mare generally looks pretty healthy, without regard to the fact that later on she looks pretty pregnant. If nature doesn't want them to catch, there's a lot of mares that will take themselves out a year. They'll cycle and do right, but they're not gonna catch. And I do think that's maybe nature's way of giving their bodies a rest by making them go barren. Try as you might to outfox Mother Nature, you're not gonna get it done."

Annette, of course, has her counterparts at other large farms, such as Gainesway, Lane's End, the Vinery, and Walmac in central Kentucky. Most of the bookers are women, and they juggle the breeding dates over the phone with their own argot as best they can. "I try to honor their first request," Annette explained, "but by the same token I may put a mare a day later than she asks. If she calls today and tells me her mare's getting ripe and asks for Tuesday, I may say to her, 'Tuesday is filled, let me put you on Wednesday morning. If we get a cancellation and I can pull you into Tuesday I will. If you find out you went stale Wednesday, let me know.' It frequently happens that the mare's follicle will be checked again and it's moving more slowly than the vet originally thought it would and that means she's not gonna ovulate for another day. So even though I may stick them a day or two later, they may want to be there anyway. Indeed, it's not uncommon to move them into the slot they originally asked for and the day before they're going to be bred they'll call and say, 'Put me back where I was. She's just not moving like we thought she would.' "

Over the years Annette also has observed that colder weather can significantly affect the ovulation cycles of the mares, especially those that have been programmed. "We may have a warm spell in February or March that brings them along and then they get stopped by a return to colder weather. Even though we fool with these mares, they still are seasonal breeders and are affected by changes in not only the amount of light but also temperature. So, colder weather will tend to put the brakes on them a little. There will be a lot of mares that may still be in heat, but the follicles may not grow because of the sudden colder weather. Still, in the end, we do manage to get almost all of them booked."

5

IN THE
BREEDING SHED

Once the mares are booked, the next step, of course, is to get them bred, which is Gus Koch's responsibility as stallion manager. As Gus and I walked into the immediate breeding area, he showed me a copy of the day's breeding schedule that Annette Couvalt had typed up the previous afternoon. Glancing over his shoulder, I could see that ten mares were scheduled to be bred to the likes of Devil's Bag, Mr. Prospector, Danzig, Forty Niner, Seeking the Gold, Private Account, Ferdinand, Topsider, Proper Reality, and Cox's Ridge. Adding up their various stud fees, I realized that the total value of the next hour's breeding session would be over a half million dollars!

After each mare's name on the list, Gus filled me in, was a reproductive code designed to help the men in the breeding shed know what kind of mare they would be dealing with: (M) was for maiden mares; (B) for barren mares; (9) for those mares being bred back on their first foal heat; (SL) for mares who had slipped or aborted their foals; (F2) for those mares being bred back on their second foal heat; (NB) for those mares not bred the year before; and finally (2) for those mares that were being "doubled up" or bred back for the second time on the same heat cycle.

Gus explained the basic breeding procedure. "As these mares arrive, Wayne Logan is up front with the teaser making sure they're in heat. He's wrapping their tail and washing them too. Meanwhile, three men will go up to the stallion barn to bring them down to us. We usually get three stallions ready at a time and call them into the breeding shed in a specific order. I always get the mare first, look to see who she's going to, and then call for that stallion. You have to double-check the names of the mares because a lot of times their names are pretty similar. You don't want to breed to the wrong stud."

The first mare on the day's agenda was Star de Gras, a barren mare coming in from Kinghaven Farm in Lexington and slated for Devil's Bag. "This mare didn't conceive last year and the people who own her live in Florida," Gus explained the logistics. "So they sent her to Kinghaven for the spring to get her bred to Devil's Bag." As Gus talked, he and the rest of the breeding crew slipped on pairs of disposable latex gloves. Proper hygiene is particularly important at a large breeding farm like Claiborne in order to protect both the incoming mares and the stallions from infection. Before every breeding the stallion's penis is washed with soap and water, and afterward he's sponged with a disinfectant. "As many horses as we handle, all it would take is one bad mare to spread an infection," Gus reflected. "We don't want to be passing anything on."

Star de Gras, a refined-looking bay mare, was now led into the barn so the breeding crew could prepare her for Devil's Bag. After Gus verified her identity, Tommy Walton, the *head* man, put a twitch over the mare's nose and gradually tightened it until he had a snug hold. The twitch is a wooden handle with a six-inch rope loop attached to one end. By firmly twisting the handle, Tommy can, if necessary, increase the torque on a cantankerous mare's nose and generally direct her head and body movement in such a way that she can't get a straight shot at kicking the stallion. Basically the twitch protects the stallion's vulnerable back legs and genitals while he is reared up in a breeding position.

Besides being twitched, every mare normally has her left front foot lifted up off the ground with a leather strap before the stallion mounts. Gus explained his role as the *leg* man. "If she's worried about maintaining her own balance, she's even less likely to kick out at the stallion. But these are big animals and anything can happen."

While Gus and Tommy twitched and strapped Star de Gras, Bobby Anderson, the fifty-seven-year-old *stallion* foreman, was busy warming up Devil's Bag, who was prancing in front of the shed and beginning to get an erection, or, in local parlance, to *drop out*. Bobby was controlling the eleven-year-old son of Halo with the help of a breeding bridle specifically designed for that purpose. The bridle features a heavy-duty bar bit that fits into the stallion's mouth with metal rings on each side to which a chain shank is attached. The two strands of the shank then converge in Bobby's hand, allowing him to control both sides of the bridle.

While the stallions, no doubt, resent the restraint imposed by the breeding bridle, it also has its allure. "When the breedin' bridle is brought out by the groom up at the barn," Bobby wryly explained the ambiguity, "the stallions can hear it jingle and they get excited because they know it's breedin' time."

Turning back toward Gus, I asked if a mare ever refused a stallion, perhaps because she didn't like the way he smelled or his vibes. "Sure. We sent a mare home the other day that was supposed to be bred to Devil's Bag. We couldn't get her bred. They said at home she showed good and they jumped her and she did fine. We got her here and, despite the twitch and the strap, she kicked by the horse and then climbed the wall. I tried her three or four times with our teaser and then we sent her home. We didn't want to get somebody hurt."

On this morning, however, commerce and propinquity were in harmony with each other. "See how Devil's Bag is nuzzling the mare and getting her ready," Gus enthused. "That's good, because you don't want a stallion that jumps on a mare and startles her. A little foreplay makes things go a lot smoother."

By the consensus of the breeding crew, Devil's Bag is the prettiest stallion at Claiborne. He is a well-balanced, dark bay with a white star on his forehead that stands some sixteen hands and, like most stallions, weighs some 1,400 pounds. A two-year-old champion, Devil's Bag was syndicated for a record $36 million and was expected to get precocious foals like himself. But his best runners so far, such as Twilight Agenda and Devil's Orchid, have tended to run to his pedigree and need more distance and time.

Devil's Bag, who was standing for $20,000, had now fully dropped out and was ready to mount Star de Gras. To the rhythm of Bobby Anderson's deft bridle work, he danced behind the mare while a groom pulled her tail aside. With a grunt the stallion jumped up on the mare while Bobby simultaneously guided his penis in. Though the crew was jaded, no doubt, by thousands of breedings, I found myself riveted. I mean, a rearing 1,400-pound stallion with a foot-and-a-half erection is hard to ignore. Devil's Bag balanced and pulled himself up on the mare by slapping his front legs against her sides as well as by grabbing her mane with his teeth. Dancing on his hind legs, he stroked until he had fully penetrated and was tightly hunched over her vulva, at which point his tail began to move up and down, or *flag*, the normal sign of ejaculation. Thus spent, Devil's Bag dozed for a moment on the mare's back before sliding off.

It had been a quick, successful cover—the way the Claiborne breeding crew likes it. While we waited for the next mare to be brought in, Bobby Anderson cautioned that not all breeding crews are alike. "At Spendthrift they have one man hold the mare, another man the stallion, and a third tell them when the stallion covers. At Claiborne I'm the man who determines when the stallion covers. While flagging almost always means the stallion has ejaculated, I also like to see him hunch into the mare that one last time. After we breed them, as you can see, Gus signs the paperwork that says who that mare's been bred to."

Since many breeding farms collect samples of their stallions' semen after every breeding by "milking" them when they dismount, I was curious why Claiborne doesn't. "That's nothing new," Gus responded. "Every breeding shed in Kentucky did it for years and years and most sheds still do, but we've discontinued it because we feel it's unnecessary and there's a chance of spreading CEM, contagious equine metritis. If a stallion is flagging good and stopping his mares, we don't need to be checking his semen all the time. Most of these farms that collect dismount samples, what they're really doing is checking to see if the horse really flagged. Testing the semen all the time is just one more intrusion upon the stallion that may tend to sour him on breeding. So we think it's better to handle him as few times as possible."

The next mare to be led in was a maiden scheduled for Danzig by the name of Fashion Delight. "You never know about maidens," Gus cautioned. "We'll have the teaser check her to make sure she isn't crazy. If Fashion Delight balks or acts up, we'll let the teaser jump her to see how she reacts. If she starts kicking or freaks out, Wayne Logan will alert me so I can tell the crew and we can be extra careful with the mare. We don't want to take a foolish chance that she might kick Danzig. He's too valuable to risk getting hurt. Like I said before, sometimes a mare acts up so much we have to send her home and wait for another day."

Given the obvious risk involved in live breeding, one would think that Thoroughbred breeders would have resorted to artificial insemination. But this practice is strictly forbidden. By universal agreement, no artificially bred horse is eligible for inclusion in the *General Stud Books* of the world. The reasons are both practical and historical. Originally, live covers were required to combat the increasingly fraudulent claims that eighteenth-century English bloodstock agents were making about the pedigrees of the horses they were selling to the emergent mercantile class. To ensure the integrity of the *Stud Book*, there had to be an instrument of control. Since only the stallion owners could guarantee the authenticity of a pedigree—that stallion Y had in fact been bred to mare X—they were the ones chosen as the custodians of the breed. Additionally, many horsemen then (and even now) believed that live covers produce superior foals because of the *élan vital*, the energy field, present during the act of procreation. Be that as it may, in the twentieth century, opposition to artificial insemination has continued, not only for these reasons but also, one suspects, for economic ones. After all, if Claiborne could, for example, fresh-freeze the sperm of Mr. Prospector and Federal Express it to any breeder who asked, Seth Hancock could drop the stallion's stud fee considerably, increase his volume, and "manufacture" a fortune.

This would, of course, put a lot of other breeders out of business, as well as quickly narrow the gene pool of the breed. The live cover requirement essentially puts a practical limit on the get of any particular stud, which may not be bad. In the short run it keeps more stallions at stud, and in the long run it ensures greater genetic diversity. And who knows? Maybe live covers do produce superior runners.

In any event, Fashion Delight was now in the breeding shed and the twitch and foot strap had been applied. She was a leggy Fappiano mare that had been sent over from Lane's End by Will Farish to be bred to Danzig, the muscular son of Northern Dancer and leading sire of 1991. Since Fappiano was a successful son of Mr. Prospector as well as the sire of Kentucky Derby winner Unbridled, the foal that would result from this $200,000 mating would definitely be bred in the purple. And if not that, certainly in the green.

But first Fashion Delight had to get bred, which today wasn't going to be easy. Wayne Logan had informed Gus that the maiden mare hadn't showed and that the teaser, Charlie, was very reluctant to jump her. Bobby Anderson, who was waiting for Danzig to be brought down, wryly speculated, "Maybe Charlie knows somethin' we don't. He probably don't want to get kicked."

Gus Koch agreed that was a possibility and, protective of his stallion, sent word to not bring Danzig down just yet. Instead he called for Charlie to be brought into the breeding shed so he could see for himself how the teaser was reacting to the mare. "Sometimes when we bring the teaser in here," Gus explained, "he'll get a little bolder and jump the mare for us."

But Charlie was still tentative. Despite Bobby Anderson's urging, he continued to warily tap-dance around Fashion Delight and keep his distance. Only after Bobby took him outside the shed and brought him back in again did Charlie finally consent to jump the mare. Since Fashion Delight hadn't actually tried to kick the teaser, Gus decided it was safe to proceed with the breeding. He signaled for Danzig to be brought down from the paddock area, where his groom had been circling him like an airplane waiting for landing instructions.

Perhaps the most valuable stallion in the world today, Danzig's success at stud was initially far from a sure thing. Yes, he was a son of the fabled Northern Dancer within whose veins coursed the blood of

Nearco, Hyperion, Native Dancer, and Mahmoud. But Danzig's female family, except for traces of Sir Gallahad and Man o' War, was
weak. And on the racetrack he earned only $32,000 and never ran
longer than seven furlongs or won a stakes. Yet what Danzig did have
in abundance was the indispensable ingredient for a successful modern stallion: blazing speed. He won all three of his races by impressive
margins, with the second horse never getting closer than 5¾ lengths.
Unfortunately, Danzig had more heart than his short, fragile front legs
could carry. After his first race, bone chips were discovered. After his
third race, X rays revealed a slab fracture in his knee and there was
nothing left but to retire him or risk his destruction on the track.
Besides the top side of his pedigree and speed, Danzig had two other
things going for him. Henryk de Kwiatkowski, his owner, and Woody
Stephens, his trainer, both believed in him. Henryk was willing to
support him with his best mares. Woody Stephens said Danzig was the
fastest racehorse he had ever trained and recommended him to Seth
Hancock for stud. Bad legs and all, it was good advice.

Now fifteen years old, Danzig—aided by the sturdier mares that
have been bred to him—has sired sons and daughters who have
earned over $30 million. In the genetic crapshoot that is horse breed-
ing, he has become a prepotent conduit. Danzig's offspring have
included champion sprinters and routers like Dayjur, Chief's Crown,
and Dance Smartly as well as multiple Grade 1 winners Pine Bluff,
Danzig Connection, Polish Navy, Stephan's Odyssey, and Green Desert. His stud fee, once only $20,000, has soared to $200,000.

A stallion's statistics, of course, are one thing; the live animal,
another. Danzig, who is blind in his right eye from a paddock injury,
came prancing and neighing into the breeding shed intent on not
wasting any time. Even though he is only 15.3 hands tall, he is not a
small stallion. He is extremely muscular and weighs over 1,400
pounds. If you thought of a prizefighter, you would probably think of
Mike Tyson. Out in his paddock he has a reputation for charging at
anyone, including his groom, who invades his turf. In the breeding
shed Danzig is so aggressive he needs to be muzzled because he has a
tendency to savage mares in the throes of his ardor.

At the trough Danzig is no slouch either. He tends toward gluttony,
and his diet has to be closely monitored. "Danzig isn't a big horse,"

Gus reflected. "But he's heavy. He's a clone of his daddy, Northern Dancer. He's wide barreled and muscled just like him. Ninety days after he got here he just filled out right away. Danzig has a tendency to get too fat. He also doesn't like to exercise, so we have to cut him back. He'd eat himself to death if we let him. We don't want to put too much weight on those legs of his, so we give him a couple of handfuls and that's plenty for him. Topsider and Proper Reality, on the other hand, never carry enough weight so we give them a little more feed. Each stallion is different and we really try and watch them."

Fifteen seconds into the shed Danzig was hot to trot. He had already dropped out, and without the restraint that Bobby Anderson was imposing on him, would already have jumped Fashion Delight. Etiquette in the breeding shed, however, is important. Commenting on Bobby's skillful control of the horse, Gus reflected, "It takes a man with good hands in the breeding shed to control a stallion. Because there's a very fine line between discipline and abuse on a stallion. Bobby has to exert just the right amount of tension on that bridle and alter the tone of his voice to control the stallion. You don't want a rogue in there, you want them to behave. But we don't want to abuse them and take away their courage and their spirit. So when a horse like Danzig comes in here, carrying on, that's his way and you don't want to abuse him. He's a very aggressive breeder. But when he hits the door we don't want him to be lunging at the mare either. We won't allow that. He's got to come in and stand there and then mount the mare. But we don't want to overcorrect, either."

Bobby, for his part, deftly did the two-step with Danzig for several minutes before allowing him to move into position and mount the mare. As the force of Danzig's weight and aggressiveness hit Fashion Delight, her legs momentarily buckled, she farted, and I thought she might go down. Danzig meanwhile was slapping the mare on the sides with his forelegs as a means of both maintaining his balance and thrusting more deeply into her. The groom who was holding the mare's tail up took a step back and told me, "You got to watch Danzig on that blind side when he's breedin' or he'll slap you in the face with one of his front feet." To which Bobby Anderson added, "If you're on his blind side, the best thing you can do is talk to him. That way he knows you're there and he won't kick you."

69

Fashion Delight meanwhile had bent and spread her legs in order to maintain her balance and stand her ground. Before she could think much more about it, Danzig had stroked her a half-dozen times, flagged, and then quietly slid off. In less than ninety seconds a $200,000 bet had been laid down. And now whether lightning had been caught in a bottle only time and luck would tell.

Even though Fashion Delight had been successfully covered by Danzig, that didn't guarantee she would immediately get in foal. Life in the breeding shed is considerably more fickle than that. Nearly 40 percent of all mares have to be bred back again before they catch. Sometimes a mare will be *doubled* back on the same heat cycle, but more often, especially with maidens, she will be bred again on her next one. "We average 1.8 covers per mare to get them in foal," Gus explained. "With some of our problem mares we have to do doubles on two heat periods. That of course brings the average way up. Fortunately, most of the time we don't have to do doubles."

Though Gus and his staff take justifiable pride in the fact that 88 percent of the mares bred to Claiborne stallions get in foal each year, I was curious about the other 12 percent. Why don't they get into foal? Wayne Logan, who had momentarily checked into the breeding shed, offered his opinion. "We get a lot of outside mares and some of the teasing crews aren't as experienced as we are. Also, some of the mares that come in here have been barren two or three years in a row, and you can't just say that it's the teasing crew or the stallion's fault. That mare has a problem. Some mares are just difficult to get in foal. Chris Evert was like that. I think Genuine Risk had a stillborn foal and they've bred her back and bred her back and never could keep her in foal either. She would be pronounced in foal and then slip them for some reason." (Genuine Risk foaled a Rahy colt in 1993.)

After Danzig was washed off and led out to his paddock, Fortunate Facts, a Sir Ivor mare, was brought into the breeding shed. She was scheduled for Seeking the Gold, a young bay stallion with tremendous potential owned by the Phipps family whose first foals would reach racing age in 1993–94. On the racetrack Seeking the Gold earned $2.3 million and a reputation as a horse with a lot of "try." He won eight of fifteen races and was a close second in six others. Some sixteen hands high, Seeking the Gold has the kind of pedigree that knowledgeable

breeders savor like a bottle of fine wine: Mr. Prospector / Raise a
Native speed on top and Buckpasser / Tom Fool stamina on the bottom. The first three generations of his all-important female family
have produced ten stakes winners. He is also inbred in the fifth
generation to three *chefs-de-race*—Blue Larkspur, Discovery, and
Bull Dog—all of which makes him an appealing outcross to Northern
Dancer and Bold Ruler–line mares.

As he entered the breeding shed, it quickly became apparent that
Seeking the Gold has a personality and style all his own. He approached Fortunate Facts chomping on the bit and "talking" up a
storm. His neck was arched, his head down, and an intermittent
chortle issued from his throat that alternated between a whinny and a
neigh. Fortunate Facts cocked her left ear and winked at him, obviously interested. But, unlike Danzig's impetuous behavior, Seeking
the Gold obviously preferred to take his time and is a devotee of
foreplay.

Bobby Anderson danced the two-step with the young stallion for
nearly five minutes before persuading him to jump the mare. Once
up, Seeking the Gold grabbed Fortunate Facts's mane with his teeth
for balance and stroked her a few times, but then, as if remembering
he didn't want to be rushed, lost interest and slid off. Bobby bailed the
stallion up again with the same results.

"He's normally a three- or four-jump stallion," said Gus, explaining
the delay. "But that's just his way. He mounts but doesn't ejaculate the
first time. They don't all come in here and ejaculate the first time. But
at least he's interested and drops out quick. Some horses come in here
and they'll just be real dozy and stand around. They're all different.
Seeking the Gold is a bit hyper and might be a stallion that should be
bred to an even-tempered mare. But he's okay. We'll get her bred, it
just takes a little longer."

While the number of jumps a stallion makes has nothing to do with
either his fertility or the success of his progeny on the racetrack, the
breeding crew is definitely partial to one-jump stallions. Gus explained why. "The more jumps a stallion makes, the more problems
that can develop. You get a maiden mare or a foaling mare that's been
away from her foal for an hour and they get a little antsy. So you don't
want them in here too long. You don't want that twitch on too long.

The quicker you get them in and out of here, the better off you are. A horse that gets to fooling around and getting up on a mare and biting her and coming off, mares get tired of that, and that's when things maybe can go wrong."

Nevertheless, Seeking the Gold continued to fool around. I edged over toward Bobby Anderson and asked him what his strategy would be if the stallion didn't flag the third time up. "With a horse like Seeking the Gold," he replied, "what happens sometimes after he goes up on the mare two or three times is he loses interest and just looks around the shed. If you take him back to the stallion barn, breed a couple of more mares, then bring him back, most of the time he'll cover better because he has his mind back on the mare again."

Gus Koch, meanwhile, reclaimed my attention by sharply slapping Fortunate Facts on her shoulder. I asked him if that was a cue to the stallion that it was time to mount. "Not really," Gus replied. "The mare's been standing there for a while and I was patting her on the neck, the shoulders, and the withers just to wake her up. Because Tommy's had her on that twitch and sometimes they'll have a tendency to focus on that pain on their nose and forget about the stallion. When the stallion gets ready to jump her again, I don't want the mare to be startled. So I'll slap her on the withers or shoulder to say 'Okay, wake up, mare, now. This is what's going on.' Rather than all of a sudden that stallion hits her and *bam*, a mare will freak out in a minute."

Gus emphasized that the breeding crew always has to be alert to the possibility that something can go wrong. "Tommy Walton's a great head man, the best we ever had. When something goes wrong, he knows which way to go with the front end of the mare. Bobby Anderson knows which way to go with the stallion. The tail man knows he's on his own, that he has to get himself out of the way when Tommy turns the mare. Besides pulling the mare's tail out of the way when the stallion mounts, the tail man will also push on the mare's hip a little if she starts coming over when he mounts. He's trying to keep the back end of the mare steady. So, it's a team job. That's real important. If the mares are good, we can breed fourteen mares in an hour."

As Gus talked, Tommy Walton listened on with interest, periodically nodding his head in agreement. Since Seeking the Gold hadn't quite dropped out enough to jump Fortunate Facts again, I asked Tommy to elaborate on the head man's job. "Basically, my job is to protect the stallion and keep him, and the other men that's in there with him, from gettin' kicked. I try to keep the mare under control as much as possible. I put the twitch on the mare and use one hand to control the twitch and then with the other hand I have a chain shank through her mouth to control her. The shank gives me a little more pull on her when I have to turn her. When a mare's gonna do something, she'll usually either hump up in the back or pin her ears back or try to move forward. You have to pay close attention when the stallion first starts to mount the mare. That's when anything can happen."

When a mare starts to kick, Tommy's first choice is to try to turn the mare's back end *away* from the stallion so that her heels clip nothing but air. But it doesn't always work that way because the mare is bigger than Tommy and may have other ideas. "Sometimes the mare will move toward the stallion"—Tommy shook his head—"and Bobby will have to get himself and the stallion out of the way as best he can. That happened yesterday morning with a maiden mare when she jumped into the wall. When her head hit the wall, it bent her neck to where her back end came toward Bobby and the stallion. So anything can happen in here, especially with them maiden mares. I've had mares rear up and strike out at me. I've had them pick me up off the ground, as big as I am at 280 pounds, and I was just hanging there, holding on to the twitch and the chain. You can control a mare to a certain extent, but if they really want to go, there's not a whole lot you can do. Them tranquilizers sometimes help, but other times it just jacks them up even more. A lot of different things happen when you do over 1,700 covers like we did in this breeding shed last year."

Working with Tommy on the front end of the mare, Gus Koch, as leg man, has to remain equally vigilant. When he picks the mare's front left leg up on every first jump, he assumes nothing and watches her ears as one means of gauging her attitude. "If I see she's relaxed and gonna stand good, I'll leave her leg down. It's a judgment call. With a stallion like Nijinsky I won't lift their leg up because sometimes it knocks the mare off balance and I don't want her throwing Nijinsky, with his bad leg, around. Other mares I'll leave their leg up with the strap the whole time they're breeding because the mare's fighting and I'm trying to protect the stallion a little bit. Then again you don't want to pull up too tight with the strap or you prop the mare and that makes it easier for her to kick. It's a dance. It has to flow in here. You have to have a crew that know what they're doing and have confidence in each other."

Tired of fooling around, Seeking the Gold decided to earn his $40,000 stud fee on the third jump. He stroked Fortunate Facts a half-dozen times and then flagged vigorously. As he was being ushered out, Danseur Fabuleux, the dam of Arazi, was brought into the shed to be bred to Mr. Prospector. Arazi, of course, was the heavy winterbook favorite for the Kentucky Derby and, off his impressive Breeders' Cup Juvenile win, was being touted as the second coming of Secretariat.

Given the importance of the next breeding, I wasn't surprised when Seth Hancock checked into the shed. He informed me that Danseur Fabuleux had been sent over from Gainsborough Farm and was coming to Claiborne for the third time. She had already produced a chestnut Forty Niner filly in 1990 and a Mr. Prospector colt in 1991. Barren in 1992, she was now being bred to Mr. Prospector again.

Mr. Prospector came paddling into the breeding shed like an old warrior. At the age of twenty-two he is a bit swaybacked and beginning to show a few ribs. Still, the sixteen-hand bay stallion remains remarkably fertile. During the previous breeding season, Seth told me, Mr. Prospector had gotten 99 percent of his mares into foal. Though age has frayed Mr. Prospector at the edges, it's hard to argue with his record as the all-time leading sire. From fourteen crops Mr. Prospector's progeny have earned over $50 million and included more than a hundred stakes winners. He is also a sire of sires, as witnessed by the success at stud of Fappiano, Miswaki, and Woodman as well as midrange sons like Crafty Prospector and Conquistador Cielo. With more runners still to come from outstanding young sons like Forty Niner, Gulch, Jade Hunter, and Seeking the Gold, Mr. Prospector's influence on the breed will not abate soon.

Of course, great things were expected from Mr. Prospector from the start. As a son of Raise a Native, grandson of Native Dancer, and out of a Nashua mare, Mr. Prospector had a solid pedigree. Even though his front feet toed out, he was the top-priced yearling when Butch Savin bought him for $220,000 at the Keeneland Select Sum-

74

mer Sale in 1971. Over the next three years, Mr. Prospector's race record was good but not outstanding. Out of fourteen races, he won seven sprints and $112,171 before breaking down. He fractured an ankle bone (a sesamoid) in a workout and was retired to Florida, where he initially stood for a modest $7,500 stud fee. At the time, it is safe to say, few anticipated the brilliance that would soon follow. Yes, Mr. Prospector had speed and class, but he was also, like his daddy Raise a Native, unsound. And even if Mr. Prospector's progeny held together, breeders wondered whether they would get a distance.

The doubts, however, were soon answered. Out of Mr. Prospector's first four Florida crops came Fappiano, Hello Gorgeous, Miswaki, Conquistador Cielo, and Distinctive Pro, and by 1980 his stud fee had climbed to $40,000. If Mr. Prospector could accomplish this with Florida mares, what would happen when he was bred to Kentucky blue hens? Butch Savin and Seth Hancock wanted to find out. Mr. Prospector was syndicated and moved to Claiborne in 1982 with an initial stud fee of $100,000.

"I had nothing to do with Mr. Prospector's success," Seth Hancock said modestly regarding his influence on the stallion's meteoric rise. "Mr. Prospector actually had some pretty good mares in Florida and was a made horse by the time he came to Claiborne."

Meanwhile Mr. Prospector demonstrated in front of us that after seventeen seasons in the breeding shed he still had both the inclination and the aptitude for his job. He talked to Danseur Fabuleux for a bit, dropped out, and then, with a little guidance from Bobby Anderson, mounted her. In less than a minute he was done. As he was being washed off, Bobby Anderson remarked, "When Mr. P breeds he's a real professional. He gets up there and does his thing. Just like Damascus. Damascus was a great horse to handle in the breeding shed too. Oh, man, he would just float on a mare. He'd breed the first time up on a maiden mare because he was so easy on them."

Pleased with the efficient way Mr. Prospector had covered Danseur Fabuleux, Seth departed to make a few calls. But before leaving he reflected on the work of the breeding crew and the million-dollar dance we had just witnessed. "You know," he stated with the gravity of someone who is ultimately responsible when something goes wrong, "this one was easy, but I couldn't do the job these men do in the breeding shed every day with three or four maiden mares, knowing what's at stake. It would make me a nervous wreck."

Two minutes later Pickled, a daughter of Cox's Ridge, was brought in and prepared. She was scheduled for Ferdinand, the big chestnut colt that won the Kentucky Derby and beat Alysheba in the Breeders' Cup Classic. Under Charlie Whittingham's patient tutelage Ferdinand earned nearly $3.8 million before being retired to stud in 1989. As a son of Nijinsky and out of Banja Luka, a Double Jay mare who produced six stakes winners, Ferdinand is well bred for both turf and dirt. Unprecocious at two, his stud fee was initially set at $15,000 in order to give him as wide a choice of mares as possible. Though it is always dangerous to predict anything about a horse, Ferdinand's progeny, like those of the Cox's Ridge mare he was being bred to, will probably do best when stretched out at three.

While Gus Koch and Tommy Walton patted and soothed Pickled, Bobby Anderson danced with Ferdinand, who had dropped out and was definitely ready to rock and roll. I asked Bobby if there was anything unusual about the stallion. "Well, Ferdinand is pretty heavy hung and when he was a young horse he would want to keep on breeding, even when the mares were tightening up on him. We had a horse here called Drone that was heavy hung and he had quite a problem that way, and sometimes we would have to jump him seven and eight times before we'd get him bred. Drone was a problem breeder on account of he had too much tool to do the job with. When a stallion is heavy hung he can only penetrate so far before he gets stopped by the mare's physical limitations. That doesn't feel comfortable to him and makes him want to back out. Of course, he can hurt the mare too."

At Claiborne and most breeding farms, the heavy-hung problem is dealt with primarily by having the tail man place a custom-made roll between the mare and the mounting stallion to keep the stallion from penetrating too far. The width of the roll varies depending on how big the stallion is. Each roll is a leather-covered wooden pin, stuffed with Styrofoam, with a handle on one end, which allows the tail man to place the roll between the stallion and the mare without putting himself in jeopardy.

Another technique that sometimes works with heavy-hung stallions is to change the angle and amount of penetration by digging a pit in the floor of the breeding shed where the stallion mounts. In recent years Claiborne has gone from a clay-and-gravel floor to a softer tan oak bark texture, which is more comfortable for the horses and easier to dig out and fill.

In any event, on this particular morning the roll was all that an ardent Ferdinand needed. As Bobby Anderson guided him over the mare, tail man Allen Atkinson smoothly slipped the roll in between the two horses. Sixty seconds later Ferdinand's work was done.

Next was West Turn, a Cox's Ridge mare that had been approved for Forty Niner. While Claiborne is proud of all of its stallions, Forty Niner is no doubt the apple of Seth Hancock's eye. The reasons are not surprising. First off, as the son of Mr. Prospector and out of File, a Tom Rolfe mare, the 15.3-hand, chestnut stallion is totally homebred. Forty Niner was conceived, foaled, and raised at Claiborne and, racing in the farm's colors, won over $2.7 million. He was a champion at two and beat Risen Star and Seeking the Gold over a route of ground at three. Forty Niner's precocity and try on the track have made him attractive to both breeders and buyers. His hefty initial $60,000 stud fee seemed more than justified when his first crop of yearlings averaged over $330,000 at the Keeneland Select Summer Sale. Claiborne is hoping that Forty Niner's first runners will do well enough not only to justify his initial stud fee but to increase it.

Forty Niner came prancing into the breeding shed ready to do his part. He quickly dropped out, jumped the mare, flagged, and slid off. As he was being washed off, I asked Bobby Anderson if the feisty little chestnut was always that avid. "He bred good this mornin' first time up," Bobby reflected. "But sometimes he picks him a mare that he don't like and we might put him up a dozen times and still not get him bred. So with Forty Niner it just depends on if he likes a mare. This year he's been less picky and we haven't had to put him up more than four times."

I asked Bobby if Forty Niner's improvement was just a case of a young stallion getting more experience in the breeding shed. "Not with Forty Niner, because when we bred him to his first test mare, he knew exactly what to do. There's some mares he just don't like. I reckon it has something to do with how they feel to him up inside. We had that old horse Alphabatim. He come in off the track and we tested him and, buddy, he fell in love with a gray mare. A bay mare come and he wouldn't have nothin' to do with her. A gray mare come in here and he would just go absolutely crazy. Secretariat and Riva Ridge retired here at the same time. Secretariat was *wham bam*, thank ya ma'am. Riva Ridge would stand there and look out and just yawwwwwn. There on the last we got him to breed a little better, but he'd still take his time to get ready. If a mare would kick at him, he'd be longer than that. He didn't have no courage."

Frosty Freeze, a feisty bay maiden by It's Freezing, was the next mare to saunter in. She was slated for Proper Reality, an In Reality colt owned by James Winn, that won ten of nineteen races and $1.7 million. "The Winns bought a lot of mares in the January sale to support Proper Reality," Gus informed me. "And they've programmed them all to be bred early to him. Once Proper Reality gets over this initial load he'll coast while some of our other stallions will be a lot busier."

A smallish, dark bay stallion, Proper Reality has a predominantly American pedigree. He is inbred 4 × 4 to War Relic, 5 × 5 to Man o' War, 5 × 5 to Balladier, and 5 × 5 to Bull Lea, which will, no doubt, make him attractive as an outcross to Raise a Native, Bold Ruler, Northern Dancer, and Ribot-line mares. Full of vim and vigor, Proper Reality came in dancing and talking to Frosty Freeze. Obviously receptive, the mare raised her tail, emptied her bladder, and winked at him. After dropping out, Proper Reality covered her on the first jump. As the mare was led out, I reflected that the product of this particular breeding was likely to win early at distances of up to a mile. The broodmare sire It's Freezing led the winners' list in 1992, primarily with sprinters. While Proper Reality won at 1⅛ mile, his best race was probably the Metropolitan Mile when he beat Seeking the Gold. Given his pedigree, Proper Reality will most likely need mares from stouter lines, such as those tracing to Ribot, Buckpasser, The Axe II, and Herbager, if his progeny are to stretch out to classic distances.

Hey Janie, a Seattle Slew mare owned by Robert Meyerhoff, was next. She was being doubled back on the same heat cycle to Cox's Ridge. "She's a maiden mare that was bred a couple of days ago." Gus filled me in. "But she didn't ovulate. She's still in heat and Doc says she still has a good soft follicle. So thinking that forty-eight hours have elapsed since then, we're gonna give her another shot here. Hopefully she'll get in foal off this cover."

Cox's Ridge came in dancing and snorting, ready to perform the honors. At 16.3 hands, he is a big, sporty-looking bay horse who won sixteen out of twenty-eight races through the age of five. Even though Cox's Ridge won the Metropolitan Mile, his foals generally need time to develop their athleticism and seem to reach their best stride when stretched out on the dirt or grass at three. His best runners have included champions Life's Magic and Vanlandingham and Hollywood Gold Cup winner Sultry Song.

Hey Janie was apparently still quite ripe because Cox's Ridge took a couple of sniffs and quickly dropped out. On the second jump he hunched up and flagged. For his part, Gus was optimistic the stallion had just earned his $40,000 stud fee. "Maiden mares are a pretty fertile group," he reflected. "We do very well with them. Barren mares are toughest. They're the ones that didn't conceive last year, and some of them have a problem and that's the reason they are barren."

Excellent Fiddle, a State Dinner mare, sashayed in. Owned by Swiss banker Walter Haefner, she had been shipped in from Ireland to be bred to Topsider. A compact son of Northern Dancer out of a Round Table mare, Topsider wasn't a great racehorse but comes from a strong female family that traces back to the great Rough Shod II. Bolstered by a strong pedigree, Topsider has gotten some runners able to get both a distance and win on the grass. Even more impressive, 82 percent of his foals get to the track and 12 percent are stakes winners. Given the Haefner connection, the foal that would result from this mating was probably destined to run on European turf. The muzzled Topsider covered Excellent Fiddle on the second jump, after which he was washed off with Furacin, an antibacterial agent that is routinely applied to all stallions bred to imported mares.

Gala Evening, a barren mare by Try My Best, was next. She was scheduled for Private Account, the 16.1-hand, bay son of the great Damascus. Private Account also comes from a strong female family. His dam, Numbered Account, is a Buckpasser mare that won fourteen races, over $600,000, and is inbred to the great matron La Troienne.

Bred and syndicated by Ogden Phipps, Private Account's runners have earned over $20 million, and he stands at Claiborne for $60,000. Now fifteen years old, Private Account's best horses have included undefeated champion Personal Ensign as well as Grade 1 winners Corporate Report, Personal Flag, Private Terms, and Secret Hello. His Damascus/Teddy blood has proved an excellent outcross, especially to Silent Screen– and Ribot-line mares.

Private Account came in snorting and sidestepping, and Bobby Anderson danced with him for a few moments until he dropped out and was ready to mount the mare. Gala Evening, for her part, took a more stoic approach. She was focused on the twitch Tommy Walton had applied to her nose and just stared ahead at the padded wall as the stallion covered her on the first jump.

As the mare was being led out and Private Account washed off, Gus observed, "She's one of these mares that needs to be sutured. The lips of her vulva will be stitched up because otherwise she'll aspirate air and be more prone to infection and losing her foal. Every year there seem to be more of them."

Gus speculated that vulva suturing has become more prevalent because of human intervention. "In nature those mares with weak vulvas, that let in too much air, would become infected and they would lose their foals, so that conformation fault would naturally be selected out. But we interfere and correct it with surgery because the mare is so valuable. So we continue that fault on and now it's gotten to where half the breed seems to have the problem."

6

WITH
THE GROOMS

With the morning breeding session completed, Gus and I walked out to check on Nijinsky II in his paddock. Allen Atkinson, his regular groom, had informed Gus that the aging stallion was walking lame. "At twenty-five Nijinsky is still fertile," Gus reflected about the old warrior. "But he's got some mileage on him. At this point in his career he's being very cautiously bred and is generally only available to syndicate members. He won't be bred to more than thirty-five mares."

Nijinsky, who would be put down two months later, was one of the great racehorses of the modern era. He won the English Triple Crown (the Epsom Derby, Two Thousand Guineas, and the St. Leger) at three, and his record as a sire and broodmare sire has been equally impressive. An atypical son of Northern Dancer, Nijinsky has become one of the paramount sources of stamina in the breed. Crossing Nijinsky to Round Table mares has been one of the hottest nicks for producing stakes winners in recent years. With several crops yet to race, Nijinsky already had more than four hundred winners with earnings in excess of $42 million when I visited. His son Seattle Dancer became the most expensive yearling in history when he fetched $13.1 million at the Keeneland Select Summer Sale in 1985. Not surprisingly, Arab and Europeans buyers have always been more fond of the turf-loving Nijinskys than Americans and it is in Europe; especially through his son Caerleon, that his male line will most likely continue. In North America, with the possible future exceptions of Shadeed, Ferdinand, and Sky Classic, his sons have been lesser lights.

When we reached Nijinsky's paddock, Gus noted that the recent winter rain had created a muddy depression just inside the gate leading into it. Worried that Nijinsky might slip or stumble and further aggravate the lymphangitis in his right rear ankle that has plagued him for years, Gus decided it was time to bring a backhoe in, scoop the mud out, and put in some fresh gravel. With several days of more clement weather predicted, he instructed Allen Atkinson to keep the open cement water tank in the paddock full because he wanted Nijinsky outside as much as possible. "We can't leave Nijinsky in his stall very long," Gus explained, "because his legs tend to stock up and swell. As long as he's out here moving a little bit, he does much better. But with Nijinsky it's touch and go. This morning Allen told me he was sound and walking fine. But now he's not."

It seemed like a scary proposition to manage a great stallion like Nijinsky who might go at any time. "Yeah, it's been scary for four years," Gus agreed. "One year we couldn't even bring him to the shed. Six years ago we had to put every mare in the hallway of the barn. That's when he was having laminitis problems with his front legs. Laminitis is an inflammation of the sensitive tissues inside the hoof. Nobody knows what causes it. It's a very painful condition because it's like having a swelling underneath your thumbnail with all your weight on it. What can happen, in the worst cases, is the coffin bone inside the hoof, because of the inflammation and all the weight it's bearing, can actually rotate and go right through the sole of the hoof. And, if it does that, he's a dead horse. Sometimes a horse will just be lame in one foot and shift most of his weight on to his other feet to ease the pain and he'll get laminitis there. Fortunately, we haven't had any trouble, knock on wood, with Nijinsky's front feet since he foundered because Wick Stone, our blacksmith, keeps on top of him. Wick gets a lot of the credit for keeping him going."

Of course, with aging stallions, if it isn't one thing, it's often another. "Nijinsky's hind leg gives us more trouble now," Gus observed, "because of the lymphangitis in his rear right ankle. You can see it looks pretty swollen. That's as small as it gets now, because he's built up a lot of scar tissue. And it still flares up every now and then. Nijinsky takes more time to take care of than all the other twenty-one stallions we have here. We don't mind doing it. But he takes a lot of care."

Later that afternoon I decided to hang out with the stallion grooms and see what else I could learn. Bobby Anderson, who has a laid-back, wry sense of humor, particularly interested me, and I talked with him as he performed his chores. A tall, back-country guy of Scandinavian descent with curly gray hair, Bobby first came to Claiborne some thirty-five years ago after quitting school in the ninth grade. He started out in the yearling section and worked five months before quitting to help out on the family farm because his father was incapacitated by arthritis. After that Bobby variously worked at Greentree, Walmac, and even put in a stint with the local fire department before finally coming back to Claiborne.

When not breeding horses for Claiborne, Bobby relaxes by restoring classic American show cars from the 1960s and '70s. His fondness for machinery, however, has a definite limit as illustrated by a story he told that sounded like a scene out of Charlie Chaplin's classic movie *Modern Times*.

"When I was about forty I took a brief break from Claiborne," Bobby recollected with an amused grin. "My brother-in-law was working at IBM and encouraged me to put my application in because of the higher wages. They called me and I took and passed all my tests and got on. I wanted to work the drill press, but they put me on the assembly line. They put me in this one room and sat me down and gave me this book and a sample typewriter that was already assembled and told me to get busy. Well, I looked at the book and got four typewriters together that day. I was really nervous and dropping pins and screws and the manager came around later that day, patted me on the shoulder, and said, 'Bobby, you done good. You got four today, but when you get real good, you'll get fifty a day.' I said to myself, If I get out out of this place today, I won't be back tomorrow."

Chastened by his IBM experience, Bobby returned to the Claiborne yearling section in 1975. A few years later he heard there was an opening in the stallion section and asked about it. Before long Bobby was grooming three stallions that were all Derby winners— Riva Ridge, Secretariat, and Spectacular Bid. He didn't initially get much of a chance to see the legendary stallion foreman Lawrence Robinson hold forth in the breeding shed because Bobby's job was restricted to turning the stallions out into their paddocks once they were done breeding.

"But I was real curious what was goin' on in the breedin' shed," Bobby reminisced. "So, one day, I said to the general manager, Mr. Taylor, 'You know, I ain't gettin' much experience doin' this. I'd kind of like to get in there, maybe every third horse, where I could watch the stallions and watch the breedin' and what's goin' on. Then I could learn a little about that.' He said, 'I don't see why not.' So he started lettin' me bring in every third horse. I picked up most of what I know from watchin' Lawrence Robinson that way. He was one of the greatest stallion men in the world. Then I got it in my head that one day Lawrence he'd retire and I could handle it. So I got to watchin' these horses and watchin' him and askin' all kinds of questions about it. And that's where I picked it up."

From watching Bobby work earlier that morning, I could see that managing a young stallion in the breeding shed requires a delicate balance between tact and strength. "When you first start out with a maiden stallion—like, say, Easy Goer," Bobby agreed, "you want to kind of let him do what he wants to do. You don't want to hit him or jerk him to lose his courage. You gotta let him go along. Then say he gets three or four mares into it and makes a mistake, you can correct him. Easy Goer jumped up once in his maiden year and pawed me in the chest. I gave him a pretty good thrashing for it and I got him right now to where he minds me and he's perfect. Seeking the Gold his first year wanted to fight and rear up and paw and carry on, but now I've got him to where I'm handlin' him, he's not handlin' me."

When Bobby is forced to correct a stallion physically, he prefers to hit him with his shank across the shoulder. "You don't want to cut him across his front legs," he explained, "because that hurts too bad. You just let him know. Mostly what I found out about them is you just raise your voice, put a different tone on it, and that has a lot to do with how a horse reacts. You never had to hit Secretariat. All you had to do was raise your voice and you'd hurt his feelin's."

Stallions are also sensitive to the bit that is in their mouths. "When you've got that bit on him," Bobby explained, "you can put quite a bit of pressure on a stallion when you pull down on that jaw. That means a lot to him. Just like a jockey can control a horse out on the track, you can get a stallion to mind you and be well mannered in the breedin' shed with a good bit. Teaching a stallion is really not so much brute strength but in your hands and voice. I don't put no weight on the horse, really. I reckon that's what people mean when they say I have good hands."

Bobby talked about the various stallions he's worked with. "Mr. Prospector is a pro. He's twenty-two years old now. He comes in and wraps things up in thirty seconds. But he was a lot cagier when he was younger. Danzig will still lunge at a mare if you let him, but Private Account won't. Private Account, you have to let him drop out pretty good before you put him up on a mare. If you put him up too soon, he'll go down. So with him you have to let him stand there and get to bouncing and then he'll mount and breed the first time up."

I asked Bobby to talk about shy breeders. "What I call a shy breeder is a stallion that comes into the breeding shed and he's not dancin' and he'll just stand there and yawn and yawn and take quite a while to get ready. I reckon he's not interested in the mare. Riva Ridge was like that. Usually, if a stallion is really a shy breeder, one mare won't turn him on more than another. He won't drop out and he'll just stand there and yawn and look around."

Of all the stallions Bobby has worked with, Secretariat is his favorite. "Secretariat had the greatest personality of any Thorough-bred in the world, especially when you were showing him off to groups of people. He loved people. You'd take him out there in front of 300 to 400 people and he'd throw his head up and pose just like he was the big king. He wanted people to like him. Then some of the ladies would come up with their perfume and he'd get ready for them. I mean, he'd show them what he had. He was one of the greatest racehorses of all time. He was the prettiest Thoroughbred of all time. He was 99 percent conformation perfect. I've taken care of Buckpasser, Herbager, Tom Rolfe, Mr. Prospector, but the greatest horse I've ever been around is Secretariat. I know everybody thought he was a disappointment as a sire, but he got too many champions there in his pedigree. There was Nasrullah a champion sire, Bold Ruler a champion sire. Then he had Princequillo on his mama's side. He was a champion sire. And don't sell Secretariat short as a sire yet. He's been a great broodmare sire and he still has a shot with Risen Star. And we've got a little horse here called Academy Award out of a Mr. Prospector mare with a helluva bloodline, and he could come on and do good. Academy Award wasn't a great racehorse, but he's got a great pedigree."

Bobby cautioned that breeders are sometimes impatient and jump to false conclusions. "Everybody thought Polish Navy was comin' on strong because of the Northern Dancer line and his daddy Danzig. He's been a disappointment to people. But they got to give him until he's got four- or five-year-olds on the track to see what he can do. Sometimes the first crop isn't the best indication. Look at Devil's Bag. They kind of rushed him, expectin' great things out of him as a two-year-old sire. They had to wait."

For Bobby, the hardest part of the year is during the breeding season because the horses are being bred seven days a week and "Every once and a while you're gonna have one of those days where nothin' goes right. The stallions, for some reason, just won't get up there and cover right or we get a couple of crazy maiden mares. A little later on in the season, say in May, we hit some rough mares too. More of the outside breeders start giving their mares hormone shots to bring them into heat. They're under more pressure then because it's gettin' late in the season and they want to get their mares bred. If they hit a real rough maiden and she shows that she's just scared, they'll tranquilize her. But sometimes that tranquilizer, or whatever it is they give 'em, will make them meaner when they get here instead of calmer."

Despite all the precautions Claiborne takes, a frightened mare will occasionally panic and hurt herself. "We had one mare," Bobby recollected, "that flipped and broke her backbone and another from Calumet that flipped and busted her head a couple of years back. We also had a mare once that we put in the chute to do some vet work to, and she jumped over the chute and tore her belly up. She had to be destroyed."

Stallions aren't immune from accidents or sudden death either. Bobby recalled several unhappy incidents. "Drone got his back leg kicked in the breedin' shed. The mare had a twitch on, a strap and everything. He mounted perfect and actually was breeding her. When he started flagging, she started kicking and caught him in the stifle. We kept him in his stall, but he got worse and had to be destroyed. Hoist the Flag broke his front leg. He came in lame one day from the paddock and the vet X-rayed him and found he'd broke his front foot. Buckpasser and Herbager both had heart attacks and died in the breeding shed. Princequillo had his heart attack in the breedin' shed but died a month later in his paddock. Riva Ridge was only sixteen. They bred him, turned him out, and he dropped dead in his paddock."

The older the stallion, the more vulnerable he is. "That's the truth," Bobby agreed. "Reviewer was another. We had to build an extension on the fence in his paddock to keep him in. I was turnin' the stallions out one morning and called Doc Kaufman and told him Reviewer was lame. He had kicked through the board of the fence and broke his leg. Alydar broke his leg kicking his stall at Calumet and had to be destroyed. That hurt Calumet real bad."

Most stallions, as they get older, have trouble with their legs. "A lot of them founder," Bobby explained. "They get that laminitis. Secretariat had laminitis. He died in October after the breeding season was over. They was expectin' another season out of him, then he got a little lame and got laminitis in all four feet. But his last season he didn't slow down none. Secretariat covered a full book to the end. He'd come to that breedin' shed and breed the first time up and go to that paddock. Most times got 'em in foal too."

Wayne Logan, who at thirty is one of the younger men working at Claiborne, joined us. Besides teasing and preparing the incoming mares, he is also the regular groom for Danzig, Devil's Bag, and Proper Reality. He offered his opinion as to why Claiborne gets the great majority of mares in foal. "A lot of the work in the breeding shed is like an art. Just like with Bobby. He started down here as a groom and he watched the old guy who used to do it. I've only been here two years and couldn't do what Bobby does. I mean, anybody can come up here and feed the stallions. But for someone to get along with the horses that may be a little different and figure them out, like with Seeking the Gold and Forty Niner, it takes experience to get the job done. There's not many young people that stay in the horse business anymore, so when you find somebody that's good with the horses and cares about the horses and cleans up around the barn, that's what you want. At a lot of farms these days people are just working paycheck to paycheck and don't really care. There's some cases when you have to worry about whether they're even feeding their horses."

Bobby, who takes care of Easy Goer, Forty Niner, and Ogygian when he's not in the breeding shed, talked about what makes for a good relationship between a groom and his stallions. "I think what it is, is that the grooms get used to them and their habits. You know their habits and correct 'em. They get used to you and you to them and you don't have any problem. But you got to watch them all the time. You take Easy Goer. He was two-year-old champion, won the Belmont, and earned almost $5 million. He's got one of the best personalities goin'. But sometimes when you go up into his stall to water him, he'll lay them ears flat back on you and his eyes will change colors. That's when you got to watch him because most likely he's gonna make a lunge or grab at you. I don't know why it is, but most of the time when stallions pin their ears back their eyes change colors, and that's a sign you better watch out because they're out to get somebody."

The daily routine for Bobby and the seven other stallion grooms at Claiborne varies according to the season. Each groom normally handles three horses plus one extra from whichever man has a day off. During the first part of the breeding season, the grooms punch in at six in the morning and for the next two hours feed and water the horses. They also turn out all the stallions that aren't scheduled to be bred into their individual, two-acre paddocks so they can get some exercise, and then muck their stalls. As soon as the remaining stallions are bred, they too are turned out into their paddocks, where they remain until around two in the afternoon. At that point all the stallions are brought in, groomed, and put back in their stalls before the afternoon breeding begins at three. After that the horses are fed in their stalls and then watched over by the night crew until the next morning.

When the weather warms up in late May or early June, the daily routine is reversed. Then the stallions are turned out right after the afternoon breeding and remain outside in their paddocks until seven the next morning. The main reason the stallions are brought in at all during the summer is to keep them out of the direct heat as much as possible. "We try to keep the sun from burning their skin and the face flies from bothering them," Bobby explained. "We call them face flies because they gather all over the horses' heads and aggravate the hell out of them. It's not so bad during the day in the stalls because we have fly control systems in them. We do the same thing with the yearlings."

Keeping the stallions outside most of the time in the summer is a good idea, in Bobby's opinion, because it gives them a lot more time to exercise. "Right now, in February, they're not outside as much. If they're lucky enough not to be breeding, they go out at six-thirty in the morning and come back in at one-thirty in the afternoon. Still, that's really not that long to be exercising. I think one of the reasons the stallions are easier to get along with during the summer is that they get more exercise then."

While most of the broodmare stalls at Claiborne have dirt floors, the stallions stand on blacktop covered with straw. Gus Koch had previously explained why. "You can't get good clay anymore to patch the stalls with. Blacktop isn't as hard as concrete, it's more forgiving on the horses' legs, and they don't scrape themselves on it. When we add the straw we try to dent-roll it so the straw remains porous and the urine will go down through it."

As I watched Bobby Anderson and Wayne Logan complete their chores in the stallion barn, I was struck by how tradition is used at Claiborne as a management tool. Each stall door has the name of the current occupant as well as an illustrious predecessor inscribed on a brass plate as a constant reminder to the stallion grooms that they aren't taking care of just another horse, but a potential sire of champions. Proper Reality, for example, was in Princequillo's and Herbager's old stall. Mr. Prospector in Hoist the Flag's. Devil's Bag in Buckpasser's. Topsider in Nasrullah's stall. Ogygian in Round Table's. Majestic Light in Blenheim II's stall. Danzig in the old stall of Reviewer and Ambiorix, and Easy Goer in Secretariat's stall. The lexicon of names made goose bumps run up and down my spine.

I paused for a moment in front of Nijinsky's stall and could see that his right ankle leg was still badly swollen. He had been brought in to be groomed and fed but would soon be turned back out into his paddock for the night. Even though the Claiborne staff was trying to extend Nijinsky's longevity and productivity by keeping him out and exercising in his paddock longer than the other stallions, I could see that he wasn't a happy camper.

"Lately Nijinsky has been getting a little sour," Wayne Logan acknowledged with obvious concern. "Earlier today he wanted to lay down in his paddock, and we went out and got him up. But when we get him up, he gets angry. He doesn't like it. When a horse gets angry they usually lay their ears back and try to bite you if they can get close enough to you. So Nijinsky's doing that now. Doc Kaufman probably looked at him three times today. We've been getting him up to keep him moving and to stimulate circulation of the blood to his feet. That made him sour. Other horses get sour if they stay in their stall too long, they try to kick you and get hateful and do things they normally wouldn't do. That will happen with a horse that has a bad leg and you keep him in the stall to protect him but he doesn't like it. It's like a young kid staying in the house and being boxed in all day long for several weeks. They can't get out and they get grumpy and sour."

I wondered if a stallion ever gets so sour he refuses to breed. "There's not much that will keep a stallion from breeding, other than masturbating," Wayne responded. "They're pretty much like humans. Some of them are a little slower, but most of the time they go in there and do their job."

I was surprised to learn that most stallions masturbate. Apparently what happens is they get an erection while in their stalls or out in their paddocks and, to amuse themselves, they rub their penis up against their belly until they ejaculate. The staff doesn't generally worry about it except if a stallion habitually comes down to the breeding shed yawning and ignoring the mares. In that case what usually works is to put a metal ring around the stallion's flaccid penis that becomes uncomfortable when he gets an erection. But sometimes, as in Private

Account's case, more drastic measures are necessary. His libido is so strong that the staff has had to strap a wire brush to his belly with the bristles facing out to dissuade him from rubbing up against himself.

Claiborne also recently experimented with putting Private Account and Danzig under artificial lights at night during December and January in the hope it would get them ready for the breeding season a little earlier. Apparently the staff figured that if gradually extending the amount of artificial daylight stimulates a mare to ovulate sooner, then maybe it would also stimulate the libido of the stallion. "We aren't using the lighting program anymore," Bobby reported, "because the horses are breeding good. Whether that was the reason or not we don't know."

It was a little past four and time for Bobby and Wayne to head down the hill to the hut by the main office where the rest of the stallion grooms were getting ready to punch out. Once there, I took advantage of the situation and asked each of the men to talk about their charges.

Tommy Walton started off first. "I take care of Damascus, Vanlandingham, and the teaser," he drawled. "Plus today I have Majestic Light because Wayne Campbell is off. Damascus is twenty-eight now and he's still a great horse to take care of. He was retired in 1989 because of poor fertility, but he still looks good. I've worked down here twenty-three years and I started taking care of him when I came here. And never had a minute's trouble out of him. Vanlandingham is real easy to work with, and the teaser isn't any trouble either. I got three nice horses. Easy to do anything with. Mr. Prospector is also a nice horse to take care of. He's an aggressive breeder. But as far as grooming or catching him in his paddock and putting him up, he's no trouble at all. Majestic Light is pretty much the same way."

Since Tommy works with a lot of mares in the breeding shed, I asked him to comment on them from the perspective of their sires. "Icecapade throws some tough fillies. I haven't seen too many of the colts because he didn't stand here. Same thing with Damascus and his fillies. Private Account and Ogygian have some nice horses, but they have some tough fillies. Kendra Road by Kennedy Road was a tough filly."

Allen Atkinson, who takes care of Ferdinand, Nijinsky, and Private

Account, and is a relative newcomer at Claiborne, offered his perspective. "Each of them have a distinct personality, but I'd say they're laid back and calmer than most of the stallions. They're much better than, say, a horse like Alydar was at Calumet. His yearling colts could really be mean. When one of them tried to strike you in the face, you sometimes had to hit their legs with the shank in order to correct them. If you didn't do it, they'd just constantly be on you."

Since Alydar had an equable temperament as a racehorse, he may have been mishandled at stud. Wayne Logan emphasized that it's important how you correct a horse. "You can't just hit a horse randomly," he warned. "When you strike them on the leg you have to do it right away so they know what they did is wrong. The first time you do that they might not realize what they're getting spanked for. But if they do it again, you spank them again. Once they realize that every time they do that they're gonna get spanked, then they'll behave. It's not like a stallion thinks ahead his first time and says, Well, I'm gonna strike this groom. But once they do it and get away with it, then they remember and will try to set you up. They learn to do that. So, if you don't want them to do it, you have to correct them right away. You can't let them get away with it three times and expect them not to do it again. Topsider is by far the most aggressive horse we have. I don't know why that is, but everybody here knows that by now."

Of all the Claiborne stallions, Devil's Bag may be the smartest. "He's also a bit of a character," Wayne explained. "When you wash him, he likes to goof off. Devil's Bag likes to step on the hose and cut the water off. He does it deliberately. He's intelligent. He knows what he's doing. When we show him to visitors and open the door to his stall, he'll come over to the door and the first thing he'll do is try to pull the pin out of the board. I think he just gets bored and it's something to do. He's the prettiest horse here. A lot of tourists like him, I think, because of that white blaze on his head."

"Devil's Bag *is* a good-looking horse," Tommy Walton agreed, but more from a horseman's perspective. "What I like about him is he's very well made. He's got good balance and good conformation."

"Proper Reality is a good little horse to take care of too," Wayne continued. "He's real laid back with people. Real quiet. A lot of stallions come in off the track and they don't have that exercise and have a tendency to put weight on pretty quick. Proper Reality is a little different. He's a hyper horse in the paddock, constantly on the move. Because of that he tends to keep his weight down, so I have to give him a little extra feed. Danzig is the opposite. He's lazy and doesn't exercise out there a lot, so he gets less feed. Danzig puts most of his energy into breeding. He's pretty direct and aggressive in everything he does and one you really got to be careful with. He didn't go through all the training that these other horses did. He raced what—three times? He retired early because of his leg injury. So he arrived here younger and had more time to pick up that weight."

Bobby Anderson picked up the bit and ran with Ogygian, an unproven young son of Damascus whose two-year-olds would soon hit the track. "Ogygian hates to come in at night. He likes to be out in the paddock. He stays in Round Table's stall, which is toward the front. We used to have Forty Niner in it, but he could see the action going on in the breedin' shed and got too worked up. Ogygian is a more mellow stallion than Forty Niner, but he doesn't stamp his foals like Forty Niner or Conquistador Cielo do."

Conquistador Cielo, another son of Mr. Prospector, interested me—probably because I've cashed some nice tickets with several of his runners. Conquistador Cielo is kept with Academy Award, Believe It, the retired Sir Ivor, and Demons Begone in the Marchmont stallion barn, which has the reputation of housing the second string of Claiborne's stallion roster.

Conquistador Cielo is a classic example of a fairly good stallion getting no respect. Even though he won both the Metropolitan Mile and the Belmont, the latter win was discounted because he was the only speed, had an easy lead, and caught a weak field on an off track. Critics also pointed to what looked like a weak female family that had only produced two stakes winners in three generations. After several mediocre initial crops, the doubts about Conquistador Cielo seemed justified and breeders began writing him off as a failure. Conquistador Cielo, however, might have the last say. His 1987 crop alone included Hollywood Gold Cup winner Marquetry, Forty Niner Days, and Burnt Hills. A number of breeders now feel his $20,000 stud fee is a bargain. He might not get a champion, but he can get you a stakes winner. His foals are also precocious. They can sprint and then stretch out; run on any surface—dirt, turf, or mud.

Bobby Anderson is partial to Conquistador Cielo because "He really stamps his foals. He gets blocky little devils that look like prizefighters. They come out of those mares flexin' their muscles. They look like they been liftin' weights or somethin'."

Just before the crew punched out, Wayne Logan concluded our discussion by harking back to Seeking the Gold, who may well be the best of all the young stallion prospects. "He's definitely the most complicated guy to figure out. Even when everything is normal, he's still a little hyper. Of course, that's just him. He's headstrong. He'd be one that would reach out and try to make that extra bite or kick."

Wayne's last comment reminded me about something that had struck me as peculiar in the stallion barns. I hadn't seen any of the horses sticking their heads out of their stalls like you do on the shedrows at a racetrack. At Claiborne the tops of the stall doors are always kept shut.

"Once you start breeding these horses," Bobby Anderson explained, "their personalities change. It's not like at the racetrack. You leave their heads out of the stall here and you walk by, they're gonna grab you. You don't fool around with these stallions."

7

COMING TO TERM
(Working with Foaling Mares)

*H*alf-past nine on a Wednesday morning and Gus Koch and I were back in his Blazer cruising over to a Marchmont barn to check on some mares that had just been bred. It was a bright, sapphire blue morning punctuated by a gusting wind that had blown the earlier gray overcast away. "We have an expression here in central Kentucky," Gus quipped about the local weather. " 'If you don't like it, wait a few hours.' If the sun stays up for a couple of more days, you'll definitely begin to see it green up around here."

When we arrived at the converted tobacco barn, Jay Caswell, the lean, sandy-haired foreman, was standing next to his assistant Jerry Allen, who was putting a bridle on a teaser by the name of Chocolate. Above us a din of sparrows, driven in by the wind, flitted in and out the rafters.

While Jerry tightened up the lead rope on Chocolate, Jay related that the two men had just come from a detention barn where some newly arrived maiden mares were being quarantined. "Even though we hardly ever have a sickness or disease problem with maiden mares coming from off the track," he explained, "we quarantine them for three weeks when they first get here just to be safe. You have to take precautions because you don't want to spread anything, especially around the pregnant mares."

Meanwhile Chocolate was raring to go. Prancing and neighing, he pulled Jerry into the first stall where Seam, a bay Polish Navy mare, was waiting. The three-year-old filly had been sent down the road to Stone Farm the day before and bred to Festin, a young stallion that Seth's older brother, Arthur Hancock III, was standing. And now it was time to see if she had caught. *Bam. Bam. Bam.* Seam tattooed the stall doors with her back hooves and warned Chocolate off.

"You can see by how she's responding to the teaser," Gus noted with approval, "that Seam's probably already gone out of heat. So hopefully she'll have an early foal next year and with luck we'll have one of the first Festins."

Festin interested me. I knew he had been imported from Argentina and won over $2 million while in Ron McAnally's care. Festin's sire Mat-Boy descends from a rather exotic male line that traces back to Teddy. I asked Gus what he thought about breeding to him. "That's Seth's area," he emphasized, "but we do have all this Raise a Native blood through Mr. Prospector, Easy Goer, Seeking the Gold, Forty Niner, and Majestic Light. Then we have the Nearctic / Northern Dancer line as represented through Nijinsky, Danzig, Polish Navy, Topsider, and Ferdinand. So we have a whole lot of those two bloodlines on the farm. That makes you go out and look to find something else to cross these mares with. You need an outcross. That's one end that Festin might serve. Seth didn't breed a top-level mare to Festin, but it'll still be interesting to see what happens."

Since Arthur Hancock III lives only a couple of miles down the same Winchester Road that Claiborne is on, I thought it would be interesting to visit the "other" Hancock brother. I knew that Arthur, after a rebellious youth, had gone off on his own, started Stone Farm, and added to the Hancock family legend with such horses as Gato del Sol, Risen Star, and Sunday Silence while building his farm up to over 4,000 acres, 150 broodmares, and 8 stallions.

A big bearish, balding man of nearly fifty, Arthur Hancock is now a devoted family man who has learned how to soften, though not relinquish, his opinions with an attractive mix of Kentucky charm and self-deprecation. When I asked him about his breeding philosophy, he stressed the importance of the family tradition of outcrossing. "You know, a big part of my father's and my grandfather's success was the fact that they brought in horses from England and France like Sir Gallahad, Blenheim, and Nasrullah that were complete outcrosses. Look what Nasrullah's done for the breed. Even Northern Dancer is from that same Nearco line. At the time they came over here there was no Phalaris blood in America. I don't even think there was much St. Simon blood until Princequillo came over here. So you're talking about infusions of blood there that have been responsible, in my opinion, for America being where it is today as a producer of great horses. That's one of the reasons why the Arabs, the Japanese, and everybody else is coming to Keeneland to buy horses instead of going to Sydney or Newmarket or wherever. Because we did get that infusion of outcross blood."

Arthur is partial to outcrossing one bloodline with another because he believes that doing so acts as a kind of catalyst that creates hybrid vigor. "Hybrid vigor is interesting," he stated, then elaborated with a story about his daddy, Bull Hancock. "My father took genetics at Princeton. He said that the fruit flies that were outcrosses were always buzzing around in these jars and the plants that they outcrossed were always so much stronger and healthier. So, that's why I believe what my father taught me. I was the first Hancock to win the Kentucky Derby, and that very theory won me the Kentucky Derby. Cougar, the sire of Gato del Sol, came from Chile. He was an outcross in tail male to Phalaris blood. You gotta have luck in this game, too, but Cougar was a complete outcross. His mother had the blood of Hail to Reason and Bold Ruler and his father came from the Chaucer/Bois Roussel line. So I don't need or want any advice about inbreeding."

Arthur Hancock's opposition to inbreeding interested me because it was clear he's thought about it. "It does work sometimes," he acknowledged. "I mean some champions here in America are 4 × 4 to Nasrullah. Swale and Princess Rooney are two examples. And if you want to inbreed to immediate stakes winners that aren't really the great horse, maybe you're better off inbreeding. I don't know. But 4 × 4 to Nasrullah. That works. Some Native Dancer also works. But for me, I'm an outcross man. I'm not very smart, but I know what I want to do. And I'll tell you another thing—based on the outcross theory—I sat right here at this desk when we were breeding Ribbon [the dam of Risen Star]. We had a season to Secretariat and I used this simple theory. I said, 'Well, look. Ribbon is by His Majesty who's by Ribot. And she's out of Break Through who is by Hail to Reason. There's no Nasrullah/Bold Ruler blood, no Phalaris blood up close up in her pedigree.' Well, that Phalaris blood [that Secretariat had] is such a strong infusion that I said, 'She's free of it. It's a great outcross. Try it and see what happens. It oughta work.' I used that as a breeding theory. If I have a mare that doesn't have any Bold Ruler/Nasrullah/Nearco/Phalaris blood, I'll pour it right in there. And that's what bred Risen Star."

Well, what about Leon Rasmussen's theory that the best hybrid vigor is produced by outcrossing two separately inbred lines? Arthur looked over at me with a bemused smile and said, "Okay, I'm gonna tell you a story which sort of illustrates what we're talking about. It was New Year's Day in 1970–71 and I was sitting in the living room with Daddy down there at the house. I was working at Claiborne then. Anyhow, Daddy liked to bet on the football games. He'd call Warner Jones and they'd have two or three bets going. And Daddy and Warner bet on the Ohio State–Southern Cal Rose Bowl game. So we turned the TV on and had the fire going and everything. At the same time I was reading Leon Rasmussen's column about inbreeding in the *Daily Racing Form*. I thought it sounded great. Take a mare that was 3 × 3 or 4 × 4 to Raise a Native. That this was the way to breed the superior horse, the great champion. I'm not talking about some Group 2 winner. I'm talking about a Sunday Silence or a Risen Star. I'm talking about the heavy hitters. The Muhammad Ali, the Mike Tyson. And this is Leon's theory. So I was arguing for Leon Rasmussen. And I was always sort of an agitator anyway and kept talking and talking. And Daddy finally got fed up with me and said, 'You and Leon have a lot in

common. Neither one of you ever bred a good horse in your lives.' And
I said, 'Well, yes, that's true.'

"Then the ball game came on and we were talking about hybrid
vigor and outcrossing while watching O. J. Simpson run for three
touchdowns just about as quick as he got the ball and put the game out
of reach. And Daddy got up, I think, with a *Blood-Horse* in his hand
and threw it across the room because he had a helluva temper. He
turned around and glowered at me and said, 'You see that O. J.
Simpson. That's what I'm talking about. He's the result of hybrid vigor
and outcrossing. He's not a white man, he's not a black man, he's an
outcross. He's a hybrid.' And he stormed out of the room. And in truth,
that's right. You look at a lot of your great athletes, Kareem Abdul-
Jabbar, Muhammad Ali, O. J. Simpson . . . there're hundreds of them.
They're not total Africans or total Caucasians, they're outcrosses. I
mean, otherwise, Africa would run off and win the Olympics every
year. Right? So, there's hybrid vigor there. Superhuman hybrid vigor.
It's like those fruit flies that just slammed into that jar, the ones that
were complete outcrosses.

"So, that's what I think. I know Daddy thought a lot of Mr.
Rasmussen, and I do, too. And I know his theories are correct to some
extent. But if you're trying to breed that great horse, the heavy hitter, I
think the best way to do it is to go for the complete outcross. Especially
after a time when you finally get so inbred that you have to have an
outcross. Like when Nasrullah came over here, he was a complete
outcross. And maybe it is cyclical. To me we're at that point right now
and really have been for a while. Maybe it was just luck, but importing
Cougar from Chile won me the Kentucky Derby and I'm hoping
standing Festin will too. I'm hoping he may be the next great outcross,
the next Nasrullah, Blenheim, or Princequillo. I don't know if he will
be, but that's what I hope. I can tell you one thing—the next
Blenheim, Princequillo, or Nasrullah is on his way from somewhere. I
don't know who he's gonna be, but I hope I get him."

Arthur's enthusiasm was contagious, and we walked out to Festin's
paddock to have a look at him. Though only 15.3 hands, the chestnut
stallion looked bigger and was playfully rolling in the mud to relieve
the itch from his winter coat. "He's a little more narrow than Halo,"
Arthur observed, "but he'll fill out. Festin's got a nice short cannon

bone, well balanced with a very nice eye and head. He's got good bone and is very correct. He won the Jockey Club Gold Cup and the Oaklawn handicap. What I'm hoping for with him is that explosion of that hybrid vigor. It'll be there or it won't. We'll see. There's so much Raise a Native, Nasrullah, Northern Dancer, and Hail to Reason blood that he should be a good outcross."

Promoting Festin won't be easy for Arthur because most commercial breeders, wanting a quick return on their dollar, prefer to breed for speed and precocity so their horses can win as two-year-olds. Since Festin's foals figure to improve with age and distance, what will Arthur say to breeders who want something more precocious and that lays closer to the pace?

"Well, Festin did have speed," Arthur retorted. "A lot of people don't know that. He ran a mile in 1:34 and worked in 1:10 and change. I don't know how much speed even Nasrullah had. What I'm talking about is that outcross blood that produces hybrid vigor. It's like when you're a kid and have a chemistry set and you pour certain chemicals together and nothing happens. And then you mix two and, boy, all of a sudden you get an explosion. That's kind of what happens, I think, when you breed that great horse. Finding those chemicals."

Besides outcrossing, Arthur is a firm believer in repeating successful nicking patterns. "Some nicks work right," he asserted. "And some don't work. Look at the negative nick of Buckpasser and Bold Ruler. If you don't believe in nicks, that one is one of the best ways to prove it. If you had a Bold Ruler mare and bred her to Buckpasser, you're out of luck. And I mean good Bold Ruler mares, stakes winners. A lot of it was tried. My father, Mr. Phipps, they all tried it and it never worked. I don't think they even got a minor stakes winner."

What about positive nicks? "I think Bold Ruler and Hail to Reason blood is a good nick. For instance, take Bold Reasoning, the sire of Seattle Slew. I remember when I was still at Claiborne and talking to Bunker Hunt when we syndicated him, and Bunker made a comment. He said, 'With one granddaddy being Bold Ruler and the other Hail to Reason, we gotta have something.' And I said, 'Well, that's right.' And Bold Reasoning ended up siring Seattle Slew and Super Concorde. Too bad he ended up dying prematurely. I think Bold Ruler/Hail to Reason is a good nick either way. The Nasrullah/Princequillo nick was a good one for us. Bold Ruler/Ribot worked with Risen Star. Bold Ruler was a complete outcross to Ribbon. The other thing with Risen Star is that Ribbon was by Break Through who's by Hail to Reason, and Secretariat is by Bold Ruler, so there again you have that nick. So two things were happening with Risen Star—a complete infusion of the Bold Ruler blood and also the Hail to Reason/Bold Ruler nick."

Back in the Marchmont barn with Gus Koch, Sweet Breads was the next mare to be teased. A Secretariat mare, she had been sent over to the Vinery two days earlier and bred to Horse of the Year and Breeders' Cup Classic winner Black Tie Affair, whose sire, Miswaki, is a son of Mr. Prospector. While Sweet Breads didn't show to the teaser, she didn't try to drive him out of the stall either. Doc Kaufman, who had just joined Gus and me, considered the conflicting information and decided to palpate the mare. "I'm gonna check to see if she's ovulated, if her follicle has gone down," he said. "When we're breeding a mare, I want to see the follicle up, but after she's been bred, if she's caught, it should be down."

Doc Kaufman didn't think Sweet Breads had caught and recommended she be teased again the next day. "If she shows to the teaser tomorrow morning," Gus explained the procedure, "that probably means she didn't catch, that she's still in heat. If Doc sees that her follicle is still up, we'll tell Annette in the office and she'll call the Vinery and try to double Sweet Breads back to Black Tie Affair right away. Otherwise we'll have to wait another twenty days for her next heat cycle before we can breed her again. Doc palpates all the mares right after they've been bred as well as twenty days later to see if they're in foal. And it doesn't stop there. We continue to tease all the pregnant mares until the end of May to make sure they haven't lost their foals and come back into heat. What all this monitoring does is give us one more shot to get a mare in foal."

Having another shot is important because Thoroughbred mares are not fecund as a breed. In 1991, for example, only 60 percent of the mares bred industrywide produced a live foal. Though Kentucky's 69 percent live foal rate is a considerable improvement on the average, it's still a mystery why over 30 percent of the mares bred don't carry their foals to term. While some 10 percent of the barren mares never even conceive, a larger number of them do catch but then subsequently abort. A majority of the latter category are early slips, where for some reason the tiny embryo simply doesn't remain attached to the mare's uterine wall. With later slips, little is known because the fetus is most often either reabsorbed into the mare's body or lost out in the field where rodents devour the evidence before it can be collected. Claiborne's 77 percent live foal rate, which makes it one of the industry's leaders, is a measure of the difficulty involved in both getting and keeping a mare in foal.

We moved on to Sintanas, a Woodman mare that had recently foaled and was a prime candidate to be bred right back. "If she shows to the teaser and she's not bruised too bad and looks okay on the speculum," Gus said, "we're gonna try to get her bred on her foal heat. We're very selective on who we breed on foal heat. They used to call it the ninth-day breeding after birth, but we call it the foal heat and it's between eight and eleven days, roughly. It's still identified on the breeding sheet as a nine though because of tradition. Old-timers used to breed on the ninth day, regardless. But we make sure they're not bruised too bad or pulling urine and that the foaling wasn't too hard on them. That's why I say we're pretty selective and we have pretty good luck with it."

I asked Gus if the primary objective of breeding on a mare's foal heat is to get an earlier foal the following year. "That's what you're trying to do," he concurred. "We're trying to save time. These mares, naturally, tend to gravitate and get later on you. So if you breed them at foal heat you can actually gain a little time on them. But we don't push them too much. We'll breed a few. But most of our foaling mares are F2 mares and bred on their second foal heat, which is about eighteen to twenty days later. Those mares are bred about thirty days postfoaling."

I wondered about the outside limit. If a mare foals in May, is that too late to breed her back? "No. We'll breed May mares back unless they're very late mares. Then it depends on their age. If it's an old mare, we'll probably go on and breed her. If it's a nice young mare and we're down to the thirtieth of May, we may decide to skip her. Sooner or later with late mares you're gonna have to skip a year so you can move her foaling date up."

Gus, Jay Caswell, and I hopped into the Blazer and drove out to the fields to check on the mares that had already been turned out for the day. Along the way I learned that once the mares are out in the fields, they are regularly monitored. During the winter season they are checked before and after lunch and then again when they are brought in to be fed at three and put up for the night. After that the night man comes on between five and six in the evening and does his rounds every three hours until six the next morning. The night man doesn't feed the mares, just tops off their water buckets while he's checking on them. Later in the spring, when the grass comes up, the daily schedule changes and the mares are kept out in the fields at night. They are turned out around two-thirty in the afternoon and not brought back into the barns until the next morning.

"So these mares are pretty well looked after." Jay Caswell reflected on Claiborne's broodmare management program. "They get the best feed, best hay and straw we can buy, a roof over their heads, and free medical treatment. We got a vet right here whenever we need him. We even check the horses at night with spotlights that hook into the cigarette lighters. If people were taken care of half as good as these horses are, we'd have a lot better people in the world."

Gus Koch nodded his head in agreement but couldn't resist adding, "If people were *bred* as well as these horses are, we'd be in better shape too. We're always culling and getting rid of the bad ones around here. The mayor of Paris can't do that. He can't say 'You, you, and you, get out of here. You're not what we want here in Bourbon County.' I got an uncle that's in favor of castration. He thinks that would solve a lot of problems. Of course, I'm sure I'm on his list. That's the problem with that idea."

Jay laughed and mimicked the breeding observation of a friend of his from Virginia. "He used to look at me and say, 'Yee boy, that breedin' always shows. That poor white trash will come out of you somewhere.'"

After arriving at our destination, we passed through the sixteen-foot swinging gate into a field that was full of older, barren mares. These weren't, however, an ordinary bunch of mares, but Blue Hen matrons that had definitely earned their keep. "There's not a better group of mares in Kentucky than are in this field, except for the fact of their age." Gus Koch paid his respects. "Unfortunately, most of them are retired and the rest are pretty old. That gray mare to the right is a sister to Ruffian out of Shenanigans. Numbered Account is next to her. She was a champion and is the dam of Private Account. That's Obeah, the dam of Go for Wand, over by the fence, and Con Game, the black one, is the dam of Seeking the Gold. That other gray mare is Lucy Belle. With her is Foreseer. The two mares next to them are Special, the dam of Nureyev, and Alluvial, the dam of Coastal and Slew o' Gold."

Alluvial, who had already produced fourteen foals, particularly interested me. Never tested on the racetrack, she had been given a chance as a broodmare because of her pedigree. She was by Buckpasser and from a great female family. Her second dam, Bourtai, had produced twelve winners and five stakes winners out of thirteen foals. Though barren the previous year, Alluvial would be trying for her fifteenth foal! The twenty-three-year-old chestnut mare, Gus informed me, was slated to be bred to Academy Award, the lightly raced son of Secretariat out of a Mr. Prospector mare. Gus lauded the decision. "And that's good because it gives Academy Award a shot to be bred to a mare like that, but one that has some age on her. Alluvial might not catch [she didn't], so Seth doesn't want to put a whole lot into a season for her. But breeding a good old mare to a young horse makes sense. Or you can send a young mare to an older stallion too and try to put a little vigor into a pedigree. Seth likes to do that. The idea is, if you are going to experiment, you do it on the extremes of the productive cycle. You take an older mare and breed her to an unproven young stallion or vice versa and hope for some luck."

Gus pointed to a younger mare that had been put in with the older mares in the hopes of calming her down. She had been in the foaling barn but slipped and so had been put back out with the barren mares. "She was a maiden mare last year that we bred one time and got into foal to Ogygian." Gus elaborated on her background. "We checked her two or three times, ultrasounded her and she was in foal. We checked her in the fall and she was still in foal in September. But then she lost the foal without us knowing it. And now she's back in heat, which is good. Hopefully we won't lose much time. Maybe we can get her bred back."

The next field we drove into contained eleven pregnant mares that were due to foal in May. "Eleven is kind of a magic number around here," Gus explained. "Most of the barns have twenty-two stalls and we have two fields connected to each one with eleven mares in each field. The yearlings at Raceland are the same way. They have twenty-two-stall barns, and one man can handle eleven horses and do eleven stalls and two men can work together more efficiently than one. So we built the barns around that twenty-two number."

Gus and Jay began rattling off the names of the foaling mares in front of us. Included in their roll call were De La Rose—a champion grass mare by Round Table that Woody Stephens trained— Shimmering Star, Confidentiality, and Duty Dance. As each mare was accounted for, the two men also checked her physical condition. The only thing that seemed unusual was that several mares were rolling in the mud. "That's just their nature," Jay explained. "Horses will do that in the winter to protect themselves against the weather and the elements. Plus now, they're rolling because they're beginning to shed their winter coat. Over the next six weeks they'll be rolling even more and we'll see big clumps of hair on the ground."

After latching the gate behind us, we proceeded to an adjoining field that contained April-foaling mares. Checking them closely, Gus observed, "A month makes a big difference. You can tell these mares are due in April by how much heavier they're carrying than the May mares. Once they get this far we don't lose too many foals."

Given the very real risk of losing a foal, I wondered whether top broodmares are always insured. Gus shook his head and pointed to Honoree, a Round Table mare that Henryk de Kwiatkowski had bought for $3.8 million when she was in foal to Northern Dancer. "When he was asked about fetal insurance on the pregnancy, he said, 'I do not carry insurance.' So they dropped it in November and the foal was stillborn in February. That's why I say you have to wear long pants to play this game. Honoree has subsequently had some foals but hasn't yet come up with a stakes winner. But she's only fourteen, so she's got time and had some good-looking foals. She had Father Rooney, a horse that was stakes-placed in Europe."

I'd heard that breeders often prefer fillies when it comes to the sex of their foals and asked Gus about it. "Not necessarily. A lot of times Seth is hoping for colts because they usually have more racing potential than a filly. But he might want a filly because the mare is getting old and he might want to keep that female family going. There are some families that have good fillies, so you like to see more fillies out of them. It depends on what we already have. Seth always has an opinion about what he wants because he'll tell them at the foaling barn, 'I'd like to get a colt out of this mare' or 'a filly out of that one.' He had something in mind when he did the mating, even. But whatever sex it is, we just hope it's healthy."

While breeders obviously desire perfectly conformed foals, the flawed ones can sometimes surprise. Gus pointed to File, the dam of Forty Niner, and told an interesting story about Tuerta, her half sister that was born when Bull Hancock was running the farm. "File's part of a great Claiborne family. She's by Tom Rolfe and out of Continue, who was a Double Jay mare. Continue was also the dam of Tuerta, who was the dam of Swale. And Continue was out of Courtesy, who was by Nasrullah. So File and Continue are part of a real good Claiborne family that goes back forty years. Anyhow, to get back to Tuerta, the story is that Bull Hancock went to the foaling barn one morning right after Continue had foaled and asked the boys what she'd had. When they told him that the mare had foaled a filly during the night, Mr. Bull got mad because that was all he was getting was fillies. Then they told him, 'Boss, the filly's only got one eye.' And they said he kicked a feed tub about halfway down the barn and said, 'All I'm gettin' is fillies and now they're comin' with one eye.' And they said he left his car and walked all the way back to the office, he was so upset. Anyhow, they wound up naming the filly Tuerta, which means one eye in Spanish. And that was the dam of Swale. So, isn't that funny, the way things happen? Bull was mad because he was getting all these fillies and especially because he had just gotten one born with only one eye. And that's the mare that produced a Kentucky Derby winner!"

A few minutes later Gus dropped Jay Caswell off at one of the Marchmont barns and then the two of us headed back to the

Claiborne side to check out some foaling mares that were only a day or two short of delivering. Along the way I shifted our talk toward the precarious local economy and the tobacco crop that would soon be planted. "Horses are in a recession right now." Gus pulled no punches. "And the tobacco industry is in serious trouble too. Most of the farmers around here are tobacco farmers, and nobody knows what's gonna happen. The government is talking out of both sides of its mouth. They're telling people not to smoke at the same time they're subsidizing the burley tobacco farmers. So how long will that keep up? Something's gonna give there."

While the government has tried to find alternative crops for local farmers to grow, in order to wean them from dependence on tobacco as their sole source of income, so far the results haven't been encouraging. About the only thing local farmers will agree about the subsidy/quota system is that they'd like to see the tobacco subsidy maintained and the quota increased.

"But part of accepting a tobacco subsidy," Gus observed, "is that you have to accept the quota. You can only grow as many pounds as they'll let you. And maybe that's not so bad. A lot of the land around here has been rotated and kept fallow because so much of it has been taken out of production by the quota system. So it's really fertile. Up in Ohio with wheat, the quota system is based on acreage. They'll come out and measure your land and you're only allowed so many acres to grow on. But if you can expand your yield per acre, you're not penalized. With tobacco it's done by poundage, so you can't expand your yield."

With its roughly sixty-acre allotment, Claiborne is one of the biggest tobacco producers in Bourbon County. All the tobacco is grown on a sharecropping basis by Claiborne employees. Typically, one of the foremen will get two men who are compatible and interested in some extra income to volunteer. After they've finished their regular shift, the men chosen will work together in the afternoons and on their days off and grow three to five acres of tobacco on halves with Claiborne, minus expenses. Gus explained the advantages of this system. "The men provide all of the labor. They also hire other men that work on the farm to help put the crop out and to harvest and cure it. It works out good. The men make some extra money and Claiborne doesn't have the headache of trying to manage this crop because it's so labor intensive."

A few minutes later we pulled up to Barn 8 where Gus wanted to check some February-foaling mares that were close to dropping. Once inside the barn, I followed along as he looked under a half-dozen mares. When I asked Gus what he was doing, he replied, "I'm just checking their bag to see if they're waxing, running any milk. That's one sign they're getting close to foaling. All the mares in this barn are close enough to foaling that we keep them in smaller paddocks so we can watch them. The reason we have around-the-clock watch on the mares, at this stage, is because sometimes a mare will lay down and foal without showing any pains or getting hot. So you have to watch them all the time. Still, you can't keep these mares in the barn all day. They gotta have exercise. You can't raise a horse in a barn. The only mares we don't turn out are those we think are about to foal."

Pointing to the mare in front of him, Gus said, "This one is San. She comes from a great female family. She's a daughter of Alluvial and a half sister to Slew o' Gold. She's a little maiden mare, got little tits, but they're tight and her bag's filling out good. She's in foal to Devil's Bag, and we'll move her this afternoon over to Barn 7 because there's a chance she'll drop tonight. If you check back later this evening when James Sebastian, our foaling foreman, is making his rounds, you might get to see this mare foal."

8

BIRTH

*L*ater that night, I followed up on Gus Koch's advice and checked in
with James Sebastian. After eating dinner in town and taking a nap, I
strolled up from the Bullpen to the foaling barn at about half-past ten.
It was a calm, almost balmy evening, and along the way I reflected
that, while most of the work on a breeding farm is performed during
the day, almost all the foals are born at night. The reason is simple.
Over millions of years those foals have best survived whose mares have
given birth under the protective cloak of darkness, thus hiding them
from predators and giving them time to find their legs. For the same
reason a mare, even today, will seldom foal during a full moon.

Upon meeting James Sebastian, the first impression you get is that
if Central Casting were to send out a man to play the role of foaling
foreman, nobody could better fit the bill. A mild, bemused man in his

mid-fifties, Sebastian immediately gives you the reassuring feeling there isn't a better job in the world than helping to usher in a newborn foal and that he and his taciturn assistant of nine years, "Gravy" Baber, have the most satisfying work on the farm. Each birth is not only a palpable validation of the farm's past efforts but also represents its best hope for the future. "It does give you a pretty good thrill to see a mare give birth to a foal." James quietly beamed. "You wonder what it's gonna be like and if it's the one that's gonna be the next *big* horse. Swale, Forty Niner, and Seeking the Gold: Those are all horses I helped foal."

A Claiborne employee for twenty-six years, James has spent the last thirteen of them working in the foaling barn. During the peak of the foaling season, he and Gravy may monitor as many as thirty-eight pregnant mares, each of which is kept in one of two converted tobacco barns according to her estimated time of delivery. Barn 8 is more of a holding tank and contains those mares that are anywhere from several days to two weeks away from delivery. Barn 7 is the actual "delivery room" where mares that are due and past due are kept and checked every fifteen minutes throughout the night.

The foaling process is, of course, unpredictable and requires a lot of patience. Foals, like children, come when they and their mothers are good and ready. Consequently, between making their rounds, James and Gravy hang out in a one-room cabin that is sited midway between the two foaling barns. It's a simply furnished structure with a few chairs, some well-thumbed magazines, a TV in one corner and a pot of hot coffee steaming in the other, and a series of framed photographs of legendary Claiborne personages peering down from the walls. When I asked James if he'd like his picture up there someday, he wryly observed, "Well, the history of Claiborne is up on that wall. So it'd be an honor. But the only trouble is, you got to be dead to be up there."

During the foaling season James and Gravy put in a twelve-hour shift. They work from six in the evening until six the next morning, seven nights a week, and deliver an average of 210 foals a year. Since this is their tenth season together, the two men work with a quiet efficiency that is informed by having seen the same mares foal numerous times before. About the longevity and productivity of the typical broodmare James was circumspect. "That's hard to say. We've had some mares go twenty-four years and average maybe twelve foals. But, other mares will have only three or four good foals and a few only one or maybe none."

When the foaling season is over, James and Gravy switch back to a daylight shift and work with twenty-five to thirty of the less productive mares in order to get them ready for Keeneland's November Breeding Stock Sale. "We brush and vacuum and give them baths every day for several months. Then Wick Stone comes in and shoes them. We have to sell or retire some of our broodmares every year to make room for the maidens coming in off the track."

Since Claiborne has obviously given up on these mares, I wondered why anyone would want to buy them. "Probably because they've got a pretty good bloodline," James speculated. "I guess the buyers figure they may get lucky and get one or two good foals. That must happen because they are good mares and they do sell."

With that observation, James indicated it was time for him and Gravy to make their rounds. After draining the last of our coffee, we headed over to Barn 7 to check up on the mares that were closest to foaling. Along the way James described some of the textbook symptoms that indicate a pregnant mare is about to drop her foal. "She'll usually start walking around the stall quite a bit and that makes her hot. Usually you'll see the steam coming off her and her coat begins to look sticky, at which point we'll check on her every fifteen minutes. A lot of times the mare will stop walking just before she breaks her water. When her labor pain hits her just right, she'll break water and then lay down. Once her water breaks she usually goes right ahead with it and the foal is born within five to ten minutes. The foal is usually up and nursing anywhere from twenty to thirty-five minutes after it's born."

What about the actual birthing process? How involved are James and Gravy in helping the mare to foal? "We pull a little bit, but not a whole lot," James responded. "Normally a foal's front feet will start coming out and their head will be right on top of their front legs. Once it's born the mare usually licks and cleans her foal. We clean out the foal's nose, so it can breathe. We let them break the umbilical on their own and then dab some iodine on the foal's stomach on that spot. The mare will usually pass her afterbirth a half hour or so later. We pick that up and put it in a bucket and weigh it for our records."

When there's a major problem, such as a breech birth—where the foal comes out backward—James will get on the phone and call Doc Kaufman. "But normally we don't bother him. Doc usually comes in the morning, checks the foal, and resutures the mare's vulva if she's one that needs it. A lot of times we have to cut the sutures before the mare foals."

Once a foal is born, James and Gravy wait to see if it stands and nurses. "If he doesn't, we'll give him a little boost. I'll hold him up and get him on his legs a little bit. Sometimes we have to hold the mare too, to make sure she stands still long enough for the foal to nurse."

Not surprisingly, maiden mares are generally the most unpredictable. "Maidens can sometimes get a little goosey," James elaborated, "because they don't want us around their foals. Sometimes we can't get back in the stall because they're being protective of their foals and we'll have to stick a big long catch pole in there to get ahold of her. Sometimes we have to tranquilize a mare to make her stay still. But once the foal is standing and nursing, we leave them alone except for our regular checks to make sure everything is all right."

Arriving at Barn 7, Gravy slid open the big front door, while James flicked on the lights. The two men then proceeded to check the mares in each stall. Since it was still February, the barn wasn't as full as it would be at the height of the foaling season. Only three mares were close enough to foaling to be there. In the first stall was Kashan, a bay Damascus mare that was in foal to Mr. Prospector. She had been accorded that honor because out of her first six foals, she had already produced two stakes winners, including Herat, a Northern Dancer colt that won over $770,000. Kashan glanced at us then calmly went back to munching her hay. "A mare will eat hay right up until they get ready to foal," Gravy noted. "This one's probably at least another day away."

Next was Miss Hardwick, a ten-year-old Honest Pleasure mare who was in foal to Crafty Prospector. "We got a Lady Hardwick and a Miss Hardwick here, a mother-and-daughter combination," James pointed out. "They both came in at the same time and both were shipped out to Crafty Prospector to be bred. This mare probably won't foal tonight either."

San was the third mare. She was the Danzig mare that Gus Koch and I had checked earlier in the day that was in foal to Devil's Bag. San was walking around her stall but hadn't yet broken into a sweat. "San might drop tonight." James considered the signs. "But you can't always tell. She's a maiden, and some mares will look like they're ready and still not foal. She's been walking around for several days. We once had a mare that took an extra month before she foaled."

After switching out the lights and sliding shut the door, we walked over to Barn 8, the holding barn, and checked in on the fifteen or so mares there. They were still being turned out during the day and some of them had mud on their coats. In front of each stall was an index-size card giving the mare's name and the stallion to whom she was in foal. I read off some of the names: Fantastic Find to Private Account, Shocker T. to Mr. Prospector, Steel Maiden to Easy Goer, Jurisdictional to Polish Navy, Officer's Ball to Seattle Slew, and Personal Ensign to Mr. Prospector.

Personal Ensign! The last name stopped me cold. Instantly the image of her getting up on the last jump in the 1988 Breeders' Cup Distaff against Winning Colors came into my mind. Here in front of me was the champion filly that had retired undefeated. But now the silks, saddles, and pageantry were gone. As I peered into her stall, Personal Ensign was just another contented horse munching on hay with mud on her coat. Looking at her, I could see she was little more than fifteen hands, though very refined and correct.

"This is Personal Ensign's third foal coming up." James beamed with pride. "The first two were Mr. Prospector colts. Her first foal is probably with Shug McGaughey now. The Phippses, who own her, may actually want a filly this time because that will keep their broodmare band going. With a filly even if they aren't runners, if they've got good bloodlines, you can still breed them a couple of times and see what happens."

His inspection completed, James and I walked back up to the shed. Along the way he confided that he didn't think there was much chance of witnessing a birth on this night. There had been a batch of foals born the previous weekend, but now things had slowed down.

What about San? I asked. "Well, you might have a shot with San," he qualified, "but she's a maiden and unpredictable. Why don't you get some sleep and I'll call you if she goes into labor."

Three hours later I groggily answered the Bullpen phone. It was three-fifteen in the morning and James Sebastian was on the other end. "Looks like that bay mare, San, is gonna foal," he chirped. "So, if you want to see it, you better come on up."

I splashed some water on my face, jumped into my clothes, and headed for Barn 7. When I got there ten minutes later James and Gravy were already with San in the back of her stall. San took one look at me and tried to walk out the open door. "Whoa. Get back in here," James genially admonished his charge while nudging her back into the stall. "You got some foaling to do."

San, for her part, was exhibiting all the classic symptoms. She was wet and sweaty around her neck and shoulders, and I could see the steam coming off her shoulders and back. She was also beginning to run a little milk from her teats. "Since she's a maiden and never done this before, she don't know what's going on," James observed. "So instinct will take over here. She'll break water here in a minute. You'll see that. Water will squirt all over the place. Sometimes it'll happen while they stand. Her being a maiden, she may lay down the first time. See how she's bending down a little now, is a little weak in the front knees? That's real common when a mare's about to foal."

Thirty seconds later San knelt the rest of the way down but remained upright on her haunches. She was breathing deeply but had not yet rolled over on her side, which is what usually happens when a mare's contractions start to come. "We'll wait out here now," James said, "until she breaks water. Then I'll go in and make sure the foal's feet and head are laying just right."

"This will be our twenty-sixth foal so far this year," Gravy whispered in anticipation. But San, at least for the moment, had other plans. Unsettled by a few sudden and excruciating kicks from her foal, she jumped back up on her feet and resumed circling her stall. "She's just holding off as long as she can," James stated, "on account of she really don't know what's going on. She's just not ready to foal. Best thing now is for us to leave her and check back in fifteen minutes."

Above: PHALARIS (1913), brilliant miler and dominant speed influence in the twentieth century. Tail male ancestor of Bold Ruler, Northern Dancer, Raise a Native, and Turn-to. *Below:* ST. SIMON (1881), undefeated nineteenth-century European champion and dominant stamina (classic) influence. Tail male ancestor of Princequillo, Round Table, and Ribot.

Above: MAN O' WAR (1917), Preakness and Belmont winner. Sire of Triple Crown winner War Admiral. Best modern descendants include In Reality, Relaunch, Believe It, and Valid Appeal. *Below:* BLENHEIM II (1928), sire of Triple Crown winner Whirlaway and of Mahmoud (to which trace The Axe II, Hatchet Man, and Al Hattab). Stamina influence. Important broodmare sire in pedigrees of Nasrullah and Northern Dancer.

Above: NEARCO (1935), grandson of Phalaris and undefeated European champion. Sire of Nasrullah, Nearctic, and Royal Charger. *Below:* PRINCEQUILLO (1940), descendant of St. Simon and major stamina influence. Sire of Prince John and Round Table. Grandsire of Stage Door Johnny. Other descendants include John Henry, Wolf Power, and speed sires Meadowlake and Apalachee.

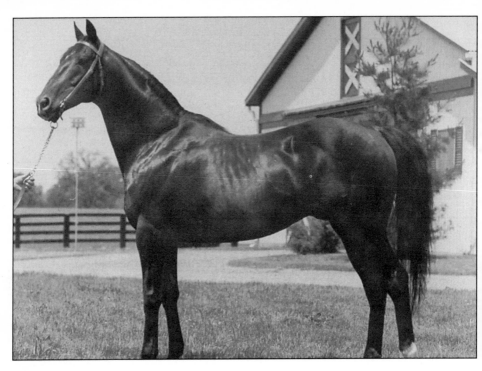

Above: NEARCTIC (1954), son of Nearco and sire of Northern Dancer, Icecapade, Briartic, and Explodent. *Below:* NORTHERN DANCER (1961), Kentucky Derby and Preakness winner. Brilliant/classic and turf influence. Sire of Nijinsky II, Danzig, Nureyev, Lyphard, Vice Regent, Sovereign Dancer, Storm Bird, Sadler's Wells, Dixieland Band, and grandsire of Storm Cat.

Above: NIJINSKY II (1967), European Triple Crown champion. Stamina and turf influence. Sire of Caerleon, Green Dancer, Shadeed, Ferdinand, and grandsire of Strawberry Road. Important broodmare sire. *Below:* DANZIG (1977), precocious sire, brilliant/classic influence. Sire of champions Chief's Crown, Dance Smartly, and Dayjur, as well as Danzig Connection, Polish Navy, Green Desert, and Lure.

Above: ICECAPADE (1969), son of Nearctic and sire of Wild Again and Clever Trick. Grandsire of Phone Trick. Primarily a brilliant, precocious line. *Below:* WILD AGAIN (1980), Breeders' Cup Classic winner. Passes on some stamina, but primarily a precocious sire.

Above: NASRULLAH (1940), sire of Bold Ruler, Red God, Grey Sovereign, and Never Bend from which Seattle Slew, Blushing Groom, Caro, and Riverman, respectively, descend. Grand broodmare sire of Mr. Prospector. *Below:* BLUSHING GROOM (1970), brilliant/classic and turf influence. Sire of Nashwan, Blushing John, Rainbow Quest, Runaway Groom, and precocious sires Rahy and Mt. Livermore.

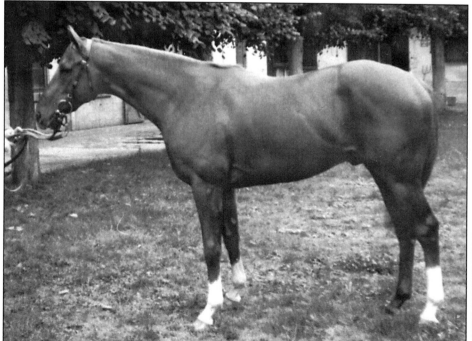

Above: BOLD RULER (1954), sire of Boldenesian, Secretariat, Bold Bidder, Raja Baba, and What a Pleasure. Best descendants include Seattle Slew, Risen Star, and Spectacular Bid. *Below:* SEATTLE SLEW (1974), Triple Crown winner, sire of champions Slew o' Gold, Swale, Landaluce, and A. P. Indy, as well as brilliant influences Capote, Slewpy, Tsunami Slew, and Houston.

Above: BUCKPASSER (1963), premier broodmare sire. Daughters have produced Private Account, Woodman, Easy Goer, and Seeking the Gold. Male descendants include Spend a Buck and Lil E. Tee. *Below:* SECRETARIAT (1970), Triple Crown champion. Sire of Preakness and Belmont winner Risen Star. Strong stamina and broodmare sire influence. Best daughters include champion Lady's Secret and Weekend Surprise, the dam of A. P. Indy.

Above: NATIVE DANCER (1950), Horse of the Year twice. Brilliant/classic influence. Sire of Raise a Native, Jig Time, and Atan; grandsire of Sharpen Up and Sea Bird; broodmare sire of Northern Dancer, Icecapade, and Ruffian. *Below:* RAISE A NATIVE (1961), sire of Mr. Prospector, Alydar, Exclusive Native, Majestic Prince, and grandsire of Triple Crown winner Affirmed.

Above: MR. PROSPECTOR (1970), all-time leading sire. Brilliant and precocious, but progeny can also stretch out. Sire of Conquistador Cielo, Miswaki, Fappiano, Woodman, Crafty Prospector, Forty Niner, and Gulch. Grandsons include Unbridled and Black Tie Affair. *Below:* ALYDAR (1975), primarily a classic influence. Sire of Alysheba, Turkoman, Easy Goer, Criminal Type, and Strike the Gold. Increasingly important broodmare sire.

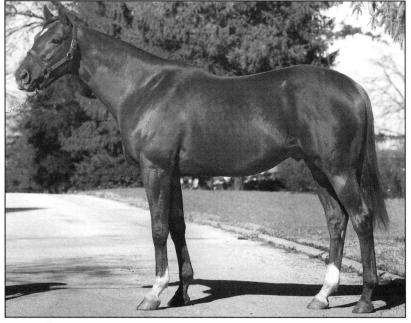

Above: IN REALITY (1964), descends from Man o' War. Primarily a speed influence. Sire of Relaunch, Valid Appeal, Believe It, Smile, and Proper Reality. *Below:* RELAUNCH (1976), brilliant, classic influence. Sire of Skywalker and Waquoit. Grandsire of Bertrando.

Above: HALO (1969), son of Hail to Reason. Primarily a classic influence. Sire of Sunday Silence and Devil's Bag. *Below:* ROBERTO (1961), European champion and son of Hail to Reason. Sire of turf champion Sunshine Forever, Kris S., and brilliant miler Lear Fan.

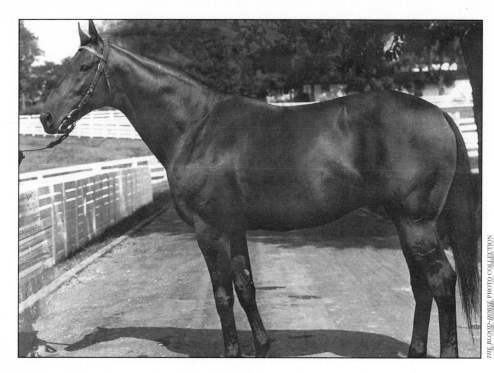

Above: RIBOT (1952), undefeated European champion and twice the winner of the Arc de Triomphe. Premier stamina and broodmare sire influence. Sire of His Majesty, Graustark, Arts and Letters, and Tom Rolfe (from which Hoist the Flag and Alleged descend). *Below:* GRAUSTARK (1963), sire of champion Key to the Mint and Breeders' Cup Classic winner Proud Truth. Broodmare sire of Kentucky Derby winner Sea Hero.

Above: HIS MAJESTY (1968), intermediate/classic influence. Sire of champions Pleasant Colony and Tight Spot, as well as Cormorant and Batonnier. Broodmare sire of Risen Star. *Below:* PLEASANT COLONY (1978), Kentucky Derby winner and champion three-year-old colt. Primarily a classic influence. Sire of champions St. Jovite, Pleasant Stage, and Pleasant Tap.

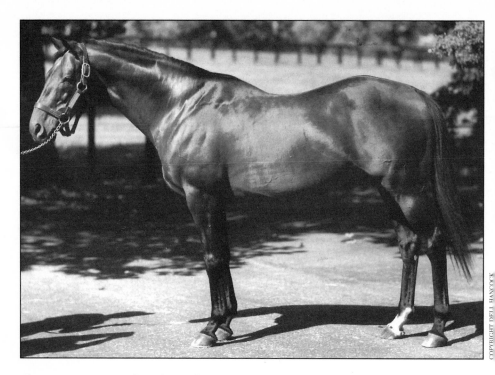

Above: DAMASCUS (1964), Preakness and Belmont winner. Descendant of Teddy line, which also produced Sir Gallahad III and Bull Lea. Sire of Private Account and the more precocious sires Bolger, Timeless Moment, Time for a Change, Ogygian, and Eastern Echo. *Below:* PRIVATE ACCOUNT (1976), intermediate/classic influence. Sire of the undefeated champion Personal Ensign, Personal Flag, Corporate Report, and Private Terms.

We turned the lights off and walked back up to the shed. Along the way I asked James what happens when more than one mare foals at the same time. "Later in the spring that's not unusual. Sometimes we'll have three getting ready about the same time. Usually one will lay down and we get everything straightened out with her and then one of us will take care of her and the other will go on to the next stall. Sometimes the mares will nicker to each other. The mares know what's happening because they can pick up on the smell. It's not unusual for several mares to look out their doors and watch the mare that's foaling."

Ten minutes later Seth Hancock pulled up in front of the foaling shack in his Blazer. It was a little past four. While I was surprised to see him, I also knew that during the foaling season he likes to check out the new foals. Seth grabbed a quick cup of coffee and joined us as we proceeded back to San's stall. Once there, Seth filled me in on the mare's background. "This mare never ran," he explained. "But because of her pedigree—she's out of Alluvial, the dam of Slew o' Gold—we decided to give her a chance. We bred her as a three-year-old."

San, for her part, had decided to lie back down and was resting calmly except for the fact that she was lifting her tail. James explained that's often a signal that a mare is about to break water. Sure enough, a couple of minutes later, San's water bag broke and James and Gravy jumped into the stall to assist her. While Gravy picked and cleaned the stall around her, James checked San's birth canal. He wanted to see if the foal was positioned correctly with its front feet coming out first and the head right behind resting on top of the forelegs. Not quite satisfied, James reached inside the mare, took hold of the foal's front feet, and gently pulled on them until they protruded out maybe six inches. "Now that we got the feet out and the head is laying right," he commented, "this should be a pretty easy foaling."

While we waited, James acknowledged that not every birth is textbook perfect. The most common problem is when the foal is upside down in the mare. In these instances the solution is normally a simple one and primarily involves manually turning the foal around while it's still inside the mare so that its feet and head are resting in the proper position.

Less frequent and more complicated are backward births, where the foal's hind legs come out first followed by its rump. In these instances the major danger is delay within the birth canal and the suffocation that can result when the foal's umbilical cord gets pinched and its oxygen supply cut off before it has a chance to breathe on its own.

Distinguishing between an upside-down and backward foal can sometimes get tricky, as Doc Kaufman later explained to me. "During a normal birth, a foal's front feet will come out first with the foot pads facing *down*, while with a backward foal the foot pads will be facing *up*. But the foot pads will also be facing up with a foal that is upside down. So you need to check the difference to make sure that the foal is backward as opposed to being upside down."

When in doubt, the way Doc Kaufman, James, and Gravy determine a foal's true position is by reaching into the birth canal and feeling for the head and the hocks. "Once you feel one of those, you know what to do," Kaufman continued. "If you have a foal coming out backward you'll feel the hocks and you need to give it as much time as you can. We put chains on the foal, get everybody ready, and then pull the foal out as quick as we can. Even then we sometimes have to give the foal some artificial respiration because that umbilical cord has been cut off longer than normal."

Of all backward births, the most fraught with peril are breech births, where the foal's rump or tail comes out first, but no feet. "Breech comes from the word britches"—Doc Kaufman explained the etymology—"because that's the area that holds everything up. You're in serious trouble when you find that because the foal can get trapped in the birth canal and you don't have any legs to grab ahold of and pull with. With breech births there's no question of what we do. James calls me and I tranquilize the mare and send her to surgery in Lexington where they do a cesarean. We call the hospital and by the time the mare gets there, they're ready for her. Fortunately, breech births are rare, and it's a pretty routine operation now and the foal and the mare are usually fine."

Fortunately, most births are normal and require only minor physical adjustments. Most common of these are when a foal gets caught at the elbow because one or both of its legs aren't extended. "That's pretty easy to handle too," James explained. "You just push the foal back in a little and pull the leg forward so both legs are even and pointed toward the opening in the birth canal."

Less frequent are foals that hip-lock. Generally these occur because the foals have very wide hips and can't pass through the mare. James and Gravy typically deal with hip-lock by putting steady tension on the foal's legs and carefully pulling it out. Again the major concern here is to act with as much dispatch as possible because of the danger of pinching the umbilical and suffocating the foal.

Despite the crew's best efforts, not all the foals at Claiborne make it. Annually between 3 and 4 percent die during birth. And of these, the most mysterious are those that are stillborn. "For some reason"—Doc Kaufman shared his bafflement—"some foals don't convert from the maternal to their own breathing. The breathing function doesn't kick in. They just never even attempt to breathe. It's kind of spooky because there's nothing you can do. The mechanism just isn't there. Thankfully, that kind of foal is pretty unusual."

Meanwhile San, who gave every indication of producing a healthy foal, suddenly stood up and began walking around the stall with her foal's feet sticking, almost comically, partway out of her uterus. James smiled at her antics without particular concern. "We'll just watch her," he reassured me, "and catch the foal if it starts to drop out."

San, who was now breathing heavily and half snorting to the contractions, reconsidered her condition and decided to lie down again. As soon as she rolled over on her side, James went behind her and gently pulled on the foal's feet. And then, quicker than I could say the word obstetrics, the slick, matted foal came out with a *whoosh!*

Quickly checking its sex, James called over to Seth Hancock, "It's a bay filly!" Then he pulled the still-sticky filly up closer to its mama's head, while Gravy cleaned the mucus from her nose and eyes. When San began to lick her foal's body maternally, I couldn't resist commenting to Seth that it was just like watching a nature film.

"That's what you like to see," Seth agreed. "But with maidens you never know. Some mares can be mean. This mare's always had a wonderful disposition and comes from a family of mares that had good dispositions. So she's probably gonna be okay. This was a very easy birth. It took all of about five minutes. We'll just let the mare lay there

now. The longer she lays there, the better it is for her. That's why
James pulled the foal up by her head, so she'd be content to lay there.
Otherwise she'd be apt to want to jump up and go see what it is.
Especially this being her first one. If she does that she has more
chance of incurring pain and laying down and wanting to roll over and
maybe accidentally injuring the foal."

James came out of the stall and indicated that the next step was to
leave the mare and foal alone so they could bond with each other.
"We'll check back in about ten minutes to see if the foal has gotten up
and begun to nurse. Some of them nurse right away, others we have to
help along."

As we walked out of the barn, Seth stressed the importance of what
we had just witnessed. "Having a new foal," he pointed out with
impeccable logic, "is the best way to start a new day because without
new foals we wouldn't have a business."

I'd heard that Seth and his wife, Debbie, were about to have their
second child, and since we were in the foaling mode it seemed
appropriate to ask him about it. "It's about a month away," he acknowledged. "Got a stall all bedded down. We won't have to go to Lexington
this time. We've got a boy named Seth Walker Hancock, Jr. We call
him Walker. I really wasn't in favor of naming him after me, but that's
what my wife wanted to do and my mother was for it. So I said, That's
fine, but we're gonna call it Walker."

What about this time, did he have a preference between a boy and
girl? "No, we've had real good luck with Walker. He's been a pleasure
and we kind of feel like we know boys now. So if it's a boy we'll be
happy. If it's a girl (Allison!), well, shoot, that'd be great to have one of
each. Just as long as it's healthy, that's all you can ask for really, as far as
any of them goes."

Back in the shed, over coffee, our conversation turned back to
horses, and Seth explained the process for submitting the names of
foals to the Jockey Club. "We usually send in the names we want in the
fall of their yearling year," he said. "But that's not etched in stone. Out
of our twenty foals of 1990, we still have four two-year-olds that are
unnamed. One of them is by Ogygian out of Prance. That's been a
tough one. You can name a foal almost anything, but we try to give
each foal a decent name. Preferably something that's short. My

mother and sister do all the naming. One-word names is kind of a farm tradition. If you use two words on a name, it's not as hard to come up with a name. Anyhow, Ogygian doesn't mean anything to us as a single name, so that's kind of stumped us. Another of our unnamed foals is by Forty Niner out of Border. We just sent in the name of Hem for her. The third unnamed foal is by Polish Navy out of Syria. And then the last one is by Mr. Prospector out of Snitch. We're still working on those."

Since we had a little extra time, I asked Seth to talk about Claiborne's racing stable. "For the most part, the goal of the racing stable is to break even. If we break even, then we're actually a little ahead because we get the luxury of having a bunch of fillies coming back to the farm as broodmares. In any given year, as many numbers as we carry, which is about fifty including partnerships, if we can break even as far as training expenses to money won goes, we feel satisfied. Then when you have a Forty Niner that knocks out a million dollars in purses, that's when you're gonna make money on your racing stable."

What about those years when the racing stable loses money? How does Claiborne pay its bills? "We make money by selling some of our yearlings at the Keeneland Summer Sale. A lot of years we don't make any money. But everybody's got a roof over their head and three squares a day and a job. It's pretty expensive to run an operation like this, and that's why we don't make any money, unless we have a real good year. But we're doing fine. We had a good year last year. We sold a couple of yearlings. We realize that it's tough times so we got to do something to keep the cash flow going. So we decided to sell a couple of our better yearlings. We sold a Danzig colt for $1.2 million and a Forty Niner filly for $725,000 and a[nother] Danzig colt for $650,000. That made our year, right there. Plus last year we had a good horse with William Haggin Perry called Scan that we sold to Japan for a little better than $3 million. We got half of that. So those things made our year."

What about the boarding side of the business? Is that a money-maker for Claiborne? "Well, hopefully, the overhead gets taken care of by our day rate. But if you break even on that you've done well. And here we don't even break even. Of course, you've got to figure I live in a big home, my mother lives in a big home, this farm supplies me with a job. So there's a lot of things to be factored in there that maybe on a smaller farm you wouldn't factor in. On a 150-acre farm, if it was my farm, I would be one of the workers, and I'd shake ten stalls a day and be up at night with the foal and wouldn't be paying myself a salary. But here it's a different setup. I don't have time to foal the mares and shake the stalls because I have to be on the phone calling people telling 'em how their foals are doing or when their mare was bred. But if this was a mom-and-pop operation, and it was my ten mares and my eight yearlings I was looking after, then I'd have that time."

A few minutes later Seth departed to catch up on some paperwork, while James, Gravy, and I headed back to the foaling barn. When we got there San was standing over and licking her foal. Though the little filly still hadn't stood up, I could see that the umbilical had been broken and that San had sloughed off her placenta. Gravy picked up the afterbirth, which was laying on the straw a few feet away, and put it into a bucket while James dabbed a little iodine on the filly where the umbilical cord had detached. Fortunately there was no umbilical hernia, a condition that afflicts some 5 percent of all foals and is typically remedied by the fastening of wooden clamps and Elastater bands to the area until it heals.

"It's a pretty nice foal," James observed. "She's not real big, but about a normal-sized foal for a maiden mare. Fillies generally are smaller than colts because the colts have a bigger bone."

Considering his options, James decided to pick San's foal up and see if it was ready to stand and nurse. Once up, the baby filly stood shakily with legs akimbo and then, when James nudged her in that direction, staggered comically toward her mother. The humor came partly from the fact that the foal was actually trying to run before it could even walk. Not surprisingly, it fell a couple of times. But James picked it up and tried again, each time deftly steadying the foal with his hands—first on one side, then the other—in such a way that it gradually began to get a sense of its balance. After ten minutes of patient instruction, James stopped. "You don't want to stress a young foal," he explained, "with too many new challenges."

Instead, James suggested we leave San and her foal to bond further and check out some other mares in the holding barn. As we walked out of the stall, San's little filly scooted after us and nose-dived down.

With an amused grin James slid the stall door shut behind us and explained there was no need to help her back up. "The foal knows it can stand up now. After she rests a little, she should get up by herself. In another half hour or so she'll probably be nursing on her own."

Twenty minutes later San's foal was standing up confidently. But as far as we could tell, it still hadn't nursed. It was time for another lesson. James entered the stall and repeatedly nudged the little filly underneath San's belly for the next fifteen minutes, hoping the foal would be able to latch on to one of her mama's teats long enough to begin sucking. But the foal was having a hard time locating anything big enough to grab ahold of with her mouth.

"After the first time they nurse, they're usually all right," James said. "Part of the problem right now is that San, like a lot of maiden mares, doesn't have a very big milk bag. Once the foal gets to nursing it'll get bigger."

Despite the delay, San was at least being cooperative. Some maiden mares will just walk away from their foals and not let them nurse at all. In those cases Doc Kaufman will be called and sometimes tranquilize the mare to get her to keep still long enough so that James and Gravy can work with the foal. But what the foaling crew does with each nonnursing mare is essentially a judgment call. When there's a delay of more than a few hours, the most common procedure is for Doc Kaufman to take some of the frozen colostrum the farm has tapped from one of the other foaling mares, thaw it out, and feed the foal to give it some temporary immunity. In addition, he will give the foal some synthetic mare's milk with the help of a stomach tube and then wait and see what the mare does over the next day or two.

Gravy, meanwhile, had been quietly observing James work with San and her foal and couldn't resist kidding him. "If you stay with that foal much longer, James, it's gonna imprint on you."

James laughed and acknowledged Gravy's point. "Normally, the first thing a foal sees," he told me, "they think is Mama. But if you stay with them too long, they can imprint on you instead. The best thing right now is probably to just leave them alone again for a while."

Two more trips to the foaling barn produced no better results. It was nearly five-thirty in the morning and I could see that getting San's foal to nurse on her nublike teats might take a while. Since I was supposed to meet up with Gus Koch in a few hours to look at some older foals, I thought it prudent to get some more sleep. But, concerned that I might go away with a false impression, James reaffirmed that for a foal to take its time before nursing was no big deal. "You like to see them stand and nurse right away. But if this little filly doesn't nurse by the time Doc Kaufman gets here at six, we'll feed her ourselves. Either way you'll probably see San and her foal over in the nursery barn later this morning."

9

IN THE
NURSERY

When I hooked up with Gus Koch later that morning around ten, he was buzzing. In anticipation of a new batch of foals being born over the weekend, Gus was planning the logistics of how to accommodate them. Over the two-way radio in his Blazer, he was alerting the foremen in the various barns to be ready for the imminent rotation of mares and foals to their new locations.

"We're going to move thirteen mares and foals out of Marchmont 6, which is the nursery barn," he told me. "These are mares that have had foals and they're anywhere from eight days to two weeks old, and now we're gonna move them into new barns and fields where they'll stay until they're weaned. That's so we have room for the next bunch of babies. We have to get the nursery barn cleaned and disinfected today, so that over the weekend, as we have more foals, we can put them back in there. This rotation of mares and foals from the foaling barn to the nursery barn and then out continues the whole season."

Gus stressed the importance of closely monitoring all the babies. As soon as a new foal is brought into the nursery barn, the first thing the staff does is to check the mucous membrane under its eyelid for jaundice. If the membrane looks yellow, that probably means the foal is having a negative reaction to some of the antibodies in its mama's colostrum, which is her first milk. Doc Kaufman will then technically confirm the presence of jaundice by doing a slide test with a microscope to see if the foal's red blood cells are glutinated.

Jaundice doesn't always show up right away, however, so each foal is checked for its first nine days. Whenever jaundice is confirmed, the foal is immediately muzzled so that it can't continue to nurse. Instead it is fed with a stomach tube for the next thirty-six hours while the mare's colostrum is milked out. Meanwhile the foal gets the immunity it needs by being given some frozen colostrum.

"What we do," Gus explained, "is steal and freeze a little colostrum from our other mares as they foal and use it as a backup bank. Once the jaundiced mare's through producing the colostrum, then we put the foal back on her milk. Typically, we get maybe two cases of jaundice out of an entire crop. Hopefully we won't get any. But we know we have one or two mares that tend to get jaundiced foals, so we watch for it."

The nursery is an extremely important barn, in Gus Koch's opinion, and he puts a premium on having good horsemen there who can not only recognize problems early but also help develop good habits in the foal. Besides checking for jaundice, the nursery staff routinely looks at each foal's navel cord to make sure it's dry and at the mare's milk bag to confirm the foal is nursing.

"If you have a sick foal here, hours can make a big difference as to whether it makes it. This is also where our foals get their first lessons. This is where we halter-break them. We do it from day one. The sooner they get used to being handled, the better. At first they're not leading very good, but they're learning and that's very important. We used to not halter our foals at birth and then when we went to lead them we had problems. If everything goes right, after nine days in the nursery barn a foal will be ready to be turned out in a group with its mama."

Gus and I moseyed over and watched Doc Kaufman work with a problem foal that had not, like the rest of the healthy foals, been turned out into an individual paddock with its mama. "This foal wasn't quite right when it was born," Doc explained as he adjusted a stomach tube that was feeding in some antibiotics. "And then it broke with diarrhea and we treated it and it lost a lot of weight. We muzzled the foal to see if the mare was giving enough milk and she wasn't. So we had two problems going on. The diarrhea and the stress on the foal because it didn't have enough milk. So we put the foal on a nurse mare, and right now it's doing much better. Meanwhile the foal's been on these antibiotics since it was born."

We moved a couple of stalls over where Wick Stone, Claiborne's ace farrier, was busy putting on some corrective neoprene shoes on a foal that had been born with crooked legs. "We had to cast this foal when it was born"—Gus gave me a quick history—"because its front legs were knuckling over. We cast him for ten days, took them off, and then he was able to stand up and get around. He's still having this problem with his toes rolling up in the air. So we'll try these neoprene shoes for a while and see if we can get some strength in his hind legs. But his right hind leg turns out so bad that he's probably never gonna be correct. And he still has a real crooked front leg. So right now, to be honest with you, this foal's chances of making it to the track don't look too good."

Given Gus's prognosis, I wondered why the farm was putting so much energy into the foal. Did it have an outstanding pedigree or belong to a major client like an Ogden Phipps or John Ed Anthony? "Foals do amazing things"—Gus offered an alternative perspective—"so we're gonna give him every chance and see how he gets along. We're gonna salvage what we can here. I mean, we've seen a lot of progress already. We even called in outside people to have him casted. We do the best we can with every foal. We can't worry about who owns the mare or who the sire is, because we need our routine to remain predictable."

Though the crooked foal was little, he was also feisty. It took two men to hold him down while Wick Stone slipped the neoprene shoes on and waited for the glue to dry. "Neoprene's a hard plastic made by Dallmer," Wick elaborated. "The shoes they make only come in two sizes, but you can still work with them. You slide them over the foot and they kind of fit like a sock. But they're stout enough so they won't pull loose when you add some glue. We'll keep these shoes on this foal for a few weeks to correct how it stands. See how this foal's right rear leg turns out forty-five degrees and it's a little crooked in the front too? We're trying to work with its legs while they're still malleable and hope it will grow out of the problem."

With up to seven hundred horses on the farm to care for, Wick Stone is a busy man. Typically he trims each foal's hooves for the first time between its sixtieth and seventy-fifth day and once a month thereafter. Most of the young horses, however, are not shod. "We don't put shoes on our yearlings"—Wick explained the farm's policy— "unless they're going to the Summer Sale or have a foot problem. Even when we train these yearlings they're barefooted and we try to keep them that way. We think a good flat foot, well trimmed and rounded without a shoe, is fine, unless there's a problem."

Doc Kaufman's curiosity, meanwhile, had got the best of him and he ambled over for a look. As we watched Wick work on the foal's tiny feet, I asked Doc what he thought about the popular belief that horses with big feet are superior runners on the turf. "Well, Round Table had a very small foot," Doc recollected, "and he was a very good turf horse. So that shoots the big-feet-on-the-turf theory to hell. But European horses run mainly on the grass, and they do have big feet. But I think that's probably the way they shod their horses, because almost every horse we get over here from Europe will have big feet. Shorty, the blacksmith who was here before Wick, used to say the feet on European horses looked like palm turtles to him. American blacksmiths tend to trim the hooves down a lot more. Maybe it's because dirt racing is harder on them, but I don't think you see as many big feet here as you do in Europe. I've also heard that horses that are kept in stalls with cement floors tend to flatten out and develop bigger feet."

Seth Hancock, on the other hand, believes the big foot theory has some validity. In an earlier conversation he had leaned toward a genetic explanation as to why he thought this was true. "I think that what you have is certain horses are good turf sires, and they may be ones who have a propensity to throw one with big feet. A horse may be a good grass horse and by a good grass sire, but probably the reason the horse is a good grass sire is because as a rule he puts a good big foot on his get."

With the big foot controversy unresolved, Gus and I hopped back into his Blazer in order to check out the healthy nursery foals that had already been turned out with their dams into individual paddocks. Along the way, he emphasized that it was important not only for the newborn foals but also for the mares to get out of their stalls and get some exercise. "The foals need to develop their muscles and coordination and the mares need to tone up and get all that junk out of their uterus. Even though we get some bad days in February and March, we still turn them out every day so we can clean their stalls. Then we decide, depending on the weather, whether to keep them out. Otherwise, if you wait around in the morning because it doesn't look good, you can wait and wait and some days you're not gonna get them out at all."

Gus pulled off by the side of the road in front of the first nursery paddock. It was a narrow, neatly fenced, rectangular paddock. As I watched the mare and foal move around inside the paddock, they began to look very familiar. "That's San, the mare that foaled last night and her filly foal by Devil's Bag," Gus confirmed my intuition. "It's a small foal but you'd expect it to be small because San is a small mare and it's her first foal. But it'll come along. It's interesting. Devil's Bag was five for five and a champion at two, yet his young horses have not been precocious. And now he's exploded with Twilight Agenda and Devil's Orchid, a couple of older horses."

Just then San ran between her foal and the fence and pinned her ears back toward another mare who was in the adjoining paddock but had moved too close to the fence. "See that," Gus approved. "That's body language telling that other mare to keep away from her foal. That mare's leaving too. There's a fence between them but San drove her away from her foal. Young mares with first foals, they're not fooling around. That's one of the reasons we isolate them for the first eight days. If you put a bunch of mares and young foals in the same paddock, you can have some heavy-duty running and maybe some injuries. So we try to protect them for the first week or so."

We moved on to a mare by the name of Isabelle D'est and her foal, who were in the next nursery paddock. As we approached she kicked the fence to warn us off and assert her territory. "Now, here's a foal that's a little knock-kneed," Gus observed. "It's turned out a little bit, a little lighter-boned than some of the foals you'll see. Not as strong. But this foal was born a little early and he'll get stronger. It's way too early to tell how well he'll do."

As we talked the little colt darted away and Isabelle D'est ran right after him. "Isn't that great!" Gus enthused. "See, she's schoolin' that foal. She's teachin' him. Then they really school them when they get 'em out in the herd there. These two were just turned out, but they'll settle down in a minute. This foal just feels good, and it's a case of Mama trying to keep up with Baby, not the other way around."

The last nursery paddock we checked contained a gray mare by the name of Bygones and a three-day-old Forty Niner foal. "Bygones is a Claiborne mare by Lyphard." Gus filled me in on the mare's background. "She was an allowance winner. This is her third foal and a filly. It's just an outstanding foal. Good size, good bone. It's correct and it's got that look that we want to see. That's what we're trying to raise here."

10

FIELDS
OF DREAM

A few moments later Gus slipped the Blazer into gear and we moved on to look at some slightly older foals that had recently left the nursery and were now being turned out with their dams—in sets of up to eleven—into much bigger fields. When we got to the first field, Jay Caswell hopped into the Blazer with us and, rather than gaze from the perimeter of the fence, we actually drove in to get a closer look at the horses. Interestingly, the mares hardly flinched when we entered, the Blazer being little more than a momentary distraction to them.

"These foals here are from ten to twenty days old, so they're still babies," Jay explained. "As you can see, we've just started to fill this field. We've only had six foals that were old enough to go in. We try to keep foals of the same age more or less together, but we don't segregate them by sex until after they've been weaned."

Pointing to the three closest foals, Gus exclaimed, "There's a Wild Again! A Danzig! And an Easy Goer! Not too shabby. And what's coming toward us is a Mr. Prospector. Last year in this very field we had two Nijinskys, five Mr. Prospectors, two Forty Niners, two Alydars, and a Mogambo. It was unbelievable. It was such a royally bred group of foals that Seth joked to Jay, 'Gus must have put the Mogambo in here.' "

What about Seth Hancock? I asked Gus. How involved is he really with the horses? Gus paused for a moment and then responded with genuine respect. "He's very involved. You're likely to see Seth riding through foals almost any afternoon. Seth knows his horses as good as any man I've ever been around. You can ride out in the field with Seth and he'll name every horse and every foal on sight. And not only name them, but he knows them. He knows their racing record, who the mare's being bred to, who that foal is by, what last year's foal was like, what the two-year-olds are doing at the track and who's training it, and who he thinks he'll breed her to next year and why. I mean, he's amazing. When you go with that man and he starts talking horses you can't beat him."

What about the actual matings? How much influence does Seth Hancock have in selecting stallions for the broodmares of clients like William Haggin Perry, the Phipps family, and Mrs. Whitney? "How much is variable," Gus acknowledged. "But Seth definitely has some input because he's so familiar with their horses and they're essentially absentee owners. Seth will see things out of mares and foals that they've had and know what kind of foals a particular stallion is getting. So he can steer them on to things or away from things they might otherwise want to do. Seth also knows what's going on at the track. He's in contact with Shug McGaughey, Bill Mott, Steve Penrod, Billy Badgett, and our other trainers. So Seth, in a lot of ways, is in a better position to make a suggestion than a client because they don't normally get to see a mare's foals."

Speaking of foals, I pointed to a brown Danzig foal that looked a little weak to me. His spindly front legs were spread out like a tripod in front of him and I thought maybe that was the only way he could balance himself. "No," Gus disagreed. "Young foals do that when they graze sometimes. See that, he just bounded away. He's fine. His dam is Qui Royally."

A bold little bay foal by the name of Recital approached us. "He's a nice-looking Forty Niner foal with good bone," Gus enthused, "out of a young Northern Dancer mare by the name of Dancealot. This is Forty Niner's third crop, and he's already had two very good crops. We really like the way they look. And it's not just us, because they sold so well that other people obviously must have liked the way they looked, too. Sometimes you can get a little partial to your own stock and other people aren't as high on them as you are. But when they go to the sale and they average $330,000, then you know other people are thinking the same thing you're thinking and that makes you feel good."

The morning and afternoon pasture inspections at Claiborne, Gus stressed, are more than perfunctory affairs. "We watch for everything out here. We're not just counting heads, but looking for injuries or if a foal's quit nursing and not gaining any weight because maybe the mare doesn't have enough milk. We're watching all that, plus how they're developing. You might even see that a mare's in heat out here. But these mares are all spread out grazing and nobody's showing. Of course, they don't figure to be because they're already past their foal heat and it's not time for them to be back in yet."

Gus pointed to a dark-brown, almost black, Wild Again foal that had a white star on its head. "He's out of a Claiborne mare that we sent to Calumet last year. He looks excellent. Look at the legs on him! He's a smart-looking individual. You can tell a lot about a foal by their expression and how they act."

I turned to Jay Caswell and asked if, based on his forty-one years of experience, he can tell which foals are going to be runners. "I still can't do that." He shook his head at the mystery. "It's just a luck thing. There's nobody that can come out here and predict that. The best trainers and jockeys couldn't do it. If we brought Charlie Whittingham and Wayne Lukas out to this field today and told them, 'Okay, pick out the best horse on this farm,' they couldn't do it. They might pick out a horse that's got good conformation, but it might be a horse that will never break its maiden. You can't measure a horse's heart just by looking at it."

"Mogambo was raised in this field." Gus gave a noteworthy example. "Right there where those foals are. He was a good-looking, flashy horse. I mean, every time you went out there you *had* to see him. He turned out to be a pretty good horse. But in the field above him was another chestnut horse that was just an average-looking horse. That was Ferdinand, and he wound up winning the Kentucky Derby and the Breeders' Cup Classic. Mogambo and Ferdinand were raised in the same barn together but in different fields. Based on looks, most people would have put their money on Mogambo."

Horse of the Year Sunday Silence is another classic example of a mediocre-looking young horse turning into a champion. Arthur Hancock III, when I visited him, had filled me in on the intimate details. "I didn't breed Sunday Silence, Tom Tatham at Oak Cliff did," he recollected. "But we raised him here at Stone Farm and had him in the Summer Sale for Oak Cliff. They had this advisor, Ted Keefer, that always hated Sunday Silence. We'd bring him out of the barn over here along with the other yearlings and Ted would say, 'Put that sonuvabitch back up. I know what he looks like.' One day Pete Logan, the farm manager, said, 'Well, you know roses look mighty good around his neck.' And Ted said, 'The only rose that will ever be on that sonuvabitch is on his grave.' Ted hated Sunday Silence so much, I think that's one of the reasons I liked him. Because I know enough to know that in this business Charlie Whittingham was right when he said, 'Never say anything about a horse until after he's been dead ten years.' For instance, Daddy put Bold Ruler on the back of Claiborne when he was a foal because he was so ugly. So you never know."

Like a lot of horses from the Halo/Hail to Reason/Turn-to line, Sunday Silence wasn't much to look at as a youngster. "He was a homely-looking weanling and yearling. He was also thin and sickly," Arthur recalled. "Our veterinarian spent all of Thanksgiving Day from two P.M. until nine P.M., missed his family Thanksgiving dinner and everything, giving Sunday Silence twenty-three bottles of fluid when he was a weanling. He'd been weaned six weeks and came down with some strange bug. He was the only one out of a hundred or so weanlings that was hit with it. The vet was so frustrated he even said, after somebody brought him a cold Hardee's hamburger for his Thanksgiving dinner about six or seven P.M. and after he had already given Sunday Silence eighteen liters of fluid, 'Why don't you go ahead and die, you little sonuvabitch.' "

But Sunday Silence was game and pulled through. "He fought through that." Arthur beamed. "Then went through the sale and I bought him back at $17,000. I took the ticket back to Tom Tatham and said, 'Here, Tom, that Wishing Well colt went too cheap.' And he said, 'Well, Arthur, we don't want him because Ted doesn't like him.' So I decided to keep him. We put him in a sale in California with a reserve of $50,000 on him and bought him back for $32,000. Then, when he was coming back here, he was involved in a van wreck and was in a clinic for about two weeks. Finally they shipped him in here, and we took him into the barn and Carl Morrison called me and said, 'This horse, he's not gonna make it. He can hardly walk.' I said, 'Well, let's turn him out in the paddock and see if he works out of it.' Sunday Silence was really sore but after four or five days he came out of it. We started back riding him about six weeks later and then I sold a half interest to Charlie Whittingham for $25,000. Charlie then sold a quarter of his half to Dr. Gaillard, and he figured he'd made a helluva deal. The rest is history. I feel like the whole thing was just fate. I mean, I would have sold him for $50,000. If he had brought in his reserve, he'd have been gone."

Looking back, there were three things that Arthur particularly liked about Sunday Silence. "First was he had fought through that illness. Then I remember seeing him run as a foal and, boy, he could fly. He was so agile, darting in and out of all these other mares and foals. Then I liked him because Keefer hated him so much. I just couldn't figure out why somebody would hate a horse that much. It irked me. I mean, if he didn't like him, he could have just said, 'That poor little fella, he's gonna have to improve a lot.' His attitude was so eerie it made me want to buck him, to prove him wrong. When I bought him back for $17,000 I bought him because I thought he was going too cheap. I really was buying him back for Tom Tatham. I was trying to be loyal. I even handed him the ticket. Tom didn't want him. So maybe I was being paid back for being loyal. It's funny how that works. Loyalty. Another time it cost me."

Arthur then related a story about how he missed out on Seattle Slew. "I never would go to the Fasig-Tipton sale when they first started here because I was a director of Keeneland. This was when Bold Reasoning had been syndicated and was standing at Claiborne. I was going to buy one of his first yearlings. But out of loyalty to Keeneland I wouldn't go to Fasig-Tipton because they had put their sale right before Keeneland's. As a consequence, I missed buying a yearling that I know I would have bought had I gone over there. Because when I worked the racetrack, I rubbed a horse named Poker for Eddie Neloy that was out of Glamour, a Claiborne mare. And this yearling at the Fasig-Tipton sale was by Bold Reasoning out of a Poker mare. The yearling, of course, was Seattle Slew, and hell, he went for $17,500. Instead I ended up buying a yearling at the Keeneland sale for $60,000 that only won two or three races. So maybe I was getting paid back, for my loyalty to Keeneland and to Tom Tatham, with Sunday Silence."

Back in the pasture at Claiborne, Gus Koch directed my attention to Top News, a Danzig mare with an Easy Goer foal at her side. "Everybody is gonna be looking at the Easy Goer foals at the sales to see how correct they are," Gus predicted. "Because he has some deficiencies in his front legs. But so far, the three we've had have been correct and have looked real nice."

I asked Gus if when Seth was breeding to Easy Goer he had tried to pick mares that would correct for his leg weaknesses. "Well, he certainly didn't want to double up on that defect. He wanted to send Easy Goer a mare that had a pretty good front end on her. This Easy Goer foal in front of us has a good set of legs on him. Much better legs than Easy Goer had when he was a baby. Easy Goer had problems from the day he was born. We didn't have to cast him or put shoes on him, but he had trouble with his left front. He had a clubby foot the whole time he was here. He would stand up, very straight on his front left foot. So what we did was keep his heels down and try to get his foot to spread out so it wouldn't get too contracted and narrow. We also did a little extra trimming on his heels, but nothing extraordinary."

What about when Shug McGaughey started to train him? "He did a great job. I'm sure Easy Goer took a lot of care at the track. And actually, it was the other leg that finally broke down and caused him to be retired. But you have to ask yourself if he was compensating for that bad leg the whole time. Easy Goer is an interesting horse. He's the kind of horse people wouldn't buy out of the sales, because they're always looking for that perfect horse at the yearling sales. But Shug McGaughey didn't have any choice. Easy Goer was a homebred of the Phippses. They raised him and gave him to Shug and he makes a champion out of him. There are no perfect horses, anyhow. You just walk through the stallion barn here and that shows you that."

Gus stressed the importance of environment in raising a good horse. "Take Raceland, for example. It's probably the best yearling farm in central Kentucky, and we own it. I say the best because just look at the size of the fields. The land rolls. It's got good grass, good barns. That's the way you raise good horses. Boy, we've raised some great yearlings out there!"

As a handicapper, I've always given Kentucky-bred horses extra consideration because of their generally superior breeding. They just seem to win more than their share of races compared to horses bred in other states. Now I realized they also have a tremendous environmental advantage because they grow up free to run in big open, rolling fields, rather than the small pastures you see in states with more expensive real estate, like California.

"Yes, sir," Gus concurred. "We can develop legs and lungs in these big open, rolling fields that can't help but give a horse an edge. Remember, we have fields here that are eighty acres. A lot of farms in other states only have twenty acres with probably as many horses on it as we do in eighty. I mean, they're basically just dry feed lots. Most people don't do things like we do. We have good water, good land, and we don't crowd our horses. We have proven stallions and great broodmares and top-level management."

Pointing to the field adjacent to us, Gus added a final exclamation point. "We also manage our land right! See that field there, we're giving it some time off. We'll probably put some cattle on it to sweeten the ground with their manure and give that pasture time to rejuvenate. Then we're gonna reseed it, because it's gotten thin in some places. But we're not gonna tear it up. We're gonna use a no-till seeder, give it a year off, and bring the horses back on it next spring."

Since the management of Claiborne's pastures actually falls into John Sosby's bailiwick, I later asked him to elaborate on Gus's com-

ments. He was not shy about singing their praises. "We are blessed
with the climate and soils we have here and that we can raise the good
grasses most of the year. You need good grasses to raise good horses.
Winters, when it dries and freezes, takes the nutritional value away
from the grass, so we supplement then with our hays and our grains."

Considering that Claiborne has been raising horses on the same
land for more than eighty years, I wondered how the farm has kept the
soil from becoming depleted. "We're very high on potassium and
phosphorus and trace elements of copper, magnesium, and so forth."
John identified the key minerals. "We have a company out of West
Lafayette, Indiana, called the Farm Clinic that's run by Marshall and
Roger Almond. They soil-sample half of our 3,480 acres each year and
tell us exactly what we need—more lime, fertilizer, and so forth.
Sometimes we spend the money on complementary grass seed. Seth,
Gus, and I look at these fields and decide which ones need a little
boost. And when it's time to reseed a field, we have a local fellow that
does custom work. He has a pasture renovator and comes in and puts
the seed in."

Interestingly, Claiborne's pastures are so fertile that there's usually
a surplus of good grass in the spring and summer. That challenge is
met by grazing cattle and periodic mowing. "As far as how much
mowing we actually do, Mother Nature governs that," John elaborated, "by the amount of rain we get. There's normally more grass in
our pastures than the horses can eat, so we do have to mow from time
to time. In April, when it's growing fastest, we purchase 600 head of
cattle and let them graze with the horses. The grass doesn't cost us
anything. It's already there. So now besides raising horses, we're
gonna make a few bucks out of these cattle, too. We usually put ten to
twelve cattle together with the same number of horses. Except we
never wean into a field that's got cattle, because if these weanlings get
to running they can get into trouble. The cattle graze until the fall of
the year, usually around six months, and then we sell them."

Besides generating extra income, the cattle are an integral part of
Caliborne's pasture management because they also eat some of the
undesirable weeds that crop up from time to time as well as sweeten
the ground. "Our goal," John concluded, "is to manage these fields so
they look great and have the right ingredients. With the right mix of

potassium, phosphorus, and clover you get two things: grazing and you fix that nitrogen back in the ground. We don't generally need to let these fields lay fallow to restore them."

Back in the pasture with Gus Koch, he pointed to a Polish Navy foal that was keeping close to its dam. "He's a little shy and hiding behind Mom. She's a maiden mare and this is her first foal. This is Polish Navy's fourth crop coming up, and he's been a little cold. So he needs to come up with a good horse, otherwise breeders will turn away from him. Those two foals over by the fence are by Slew o' Gold and Afleet. When the Afleet was born, he was right up on his toes. He's come down on his pasterns some, but still has one leg that's a little funny. But he's doing good."

As we drove back out of the field and I closed the gate behind us, I was reminded that horsemen in central Kentucky take great pride in their fencing. Driving past all the horse farms in the Lexington area, a visitor will see more board feet of rail fencing, mostly painted white, than anywhere else in the world.

Good fencing is important not only to control stock, but also as a sign of success. If the paint is chipped and peeling and the rails are falling down, it's almost a dead giveaway that the farm is on the brink of foreclosure. Unlike many of the surrounding horse farms, Claiborne avoided the spendthrift ways of the 1980s. Seth Hancock didn't mortgage the farm and overexpand in anticipation of ever higher yearling prices. Consequently, in the harsh economic climate of the 1990s, Claiborne is largely free of debt and able to afford proper maintenance.

While good-looking fencing is important, the primary consideration at Claiborne is the safety of the horses. Each gate has not only a hook clasp but also a backup chain with a spring-loaded thumb latch that even the most enterprising horse can't open. Similar precautions are taken with how the fences are constructed. All the pasture fencing has been built with the posts on the outside so the interior is totally smooth and there is nothing for a horse to catch on or trip over. Even the trees are fenced so that the posts are on the inside and the smooth side faces out.

Unlike most farms in the area, Claiborne's fencing is neither painted white nor totally constructed of wood. In recent years the farm has gone to a combination of 4 × 6 oak rail on top with a bottom that is mostly a V-wire mesh. About the advantages of wire fencing, John Sosby will tell you, "Board fence is all right. I wouldn't knock it. We use some of it too. Our posts sit on eleven feet and we have a sixteen-foot board and a five-foot board we use for a batten. But that wire is safer and more durable. We've gone twenty-five years without replacing it. I've had to replace the posts but been able to save the wire by removing the staples with the proper piece of equipment and then put it right back up."

All the fences at Claiborne are also painted with an acrylic black paint every three years to extend the life of the rail and posts. "It's cheaper to paint than to rebuild a fence," John explained. "That fence costs us about six dollars a foot to build. Since we have over a hundred miles of fence, you can see we've got a big investment there that's worth maintaining."

While the fences at Claiborne are intended primarily to keep the horses in, they also serve, along with an elaborate security system, to keep strangers out. Given the fences, uniformed employees, and a radio system that hooks up everyone on the farm and also is tied in with the local police department, it's extremely difficult for a stranger to wander around Claiborne without being spotted. Nevertheless, Claiborne did once experience a legendary case of horse thievery with international implications. The horse involved was Franfreluche, a champion mare by Northern Dancer owned by Canadian secessionist Louie Levesque.

"Franfreluche was sent down here to be bred to Secretariat in his first year at stud and she was stolen right out of that field," Gus Koch recalled as we drove along. "They put up a reward for her, and the FBI was actually involved in the case because Levesque was in politics and Quebec was trying to secede from the Canadian union and they thought it might have had political overtones. Anyhow, the state police got a tip and they found Franfreluche down in some hillbilly's backyard. She wandered into his yard one day and he actually didn't even know who the mare was. Apparently the police were getting hot on their trail, so the thieves just turned the mare loose. The guy who found Franfreluche was going to ride her in the Christmas parade. Anyhow, they got her back and the guy that stole her initially had a public defender. They brought him up here to try him for stealing this mare, and then a big-time Mafia lawyer defended him and wouldn't let him take the stand. We were hoping he would talk. He was convicted, but they wouldn't let him say a word. So we still really don't know what happened."

Jay Caswell, who had been listening quietly, elaborated on how the thieves had done it. "We went out one morning looking for Fran-freluche and she wasn't there. They just cut the fence over there and took her out. They apparently had been in a couple of times feeding these mares to draw them up to that fence. They had baited her and when they cut the fence, Billy Purcell was the guy who found her missing. He rode the fence and didn't see any holes. What they had done was very meticulously cut that wire, take the mare out, put the cut piece back up, and wrap it with fine wire. So when you drove by, like we normally do, you couldn't see the cut in the fence."

Gus Koch gave his own final assessment. "The man that took her wasn't smart enough to figure this out by himself. Somebody put him up to it. We're sure of that. We've heard he's still in jail somewhere in Tennessee on another rap. It would be great if he would talk because it would be a helluva story."

A few minutes later we dropped Jay Caswell back off at the nursery barn and headed back to the office. Along the way I asked Gus if he was much of a handicapper. "When I go to the track"—he laughed—"people think I have an advantage. Hell, I got a handicap. My loyalty to Claiborne gets me into trouble because I just can't bet against any of the horses we've raised. See, I got ten kids. I've got a big family. Now, my oldest boy is a junior in college and I have one in high school and one in junior high who's my horseman. But my kids love to go to Keeneland and beat me. I'll be betting a Claiborne horse and they'll be reading that *Racing Form* and come up with a hot horse and bet it, and they love it if they can beat their old man. They think that's great. So I'm better off just sticking to raising horses."

11

RAISING
A GOOD HORSE

*T*he next afternoon I was in John Sosby's office at about half-past three, ready to further explore the trials and jubilations of raising a good horse. The fickle central Kentucky weather, which earlier in the week had been cold, wet, and blustery, was now almost sultry. Like a proud papa, John leaned back in his chair and crooned, "You know, there's nothin' more beautiful than the birth of a foal. That's what we've strived to do, to get that foal on the ground. That little rascal will struggle there for twenty or thirty minutes and then he'll get on his feet and the next morning you go back and say, 'Well, golly, look at 'em!' And then you put a halter on him and you lead him out. The first time he goes to and from that paddock he's led just the way he's gonna be led the rest of his life."

A devoted student of horse psychology, John elaborated on the advantages of haltering a foal within a few hours of its birth. "That way he does not get man shy of you. You're his friend and you don't do anything to make him distrust you. Yes, there's a time, like with a child, that you have to discipline him. But you don't abuse him. And you don't hit my horse around the head. Just like you don't hit a kid on the head. You hit him on the rump if he needs to be corrected. We're very, very touchy about the way you treat my horse."

Once a young foal has accepted the halter, the next step is to teach it how to be turned through a gate. While horses tend to spook easily, because of their fear/flight mechanism, they are also creatures of habit and respond well to a consistent routine. Claiborne keeps that fact in mind not only in training them, but also in the physical design of the farm.

All the paddock gates in recent years, for example, have been built so that a groom can hold a horse with his right hand while opening the gate with his left. Similarly, all the stall doors in the newer barns slide open from right to left. "That way," John explained, "you don't have to reach across the horse. You slide the stall door to the left with your left hand while controlling the horse with your right hand. Then after you've turned the horse, you can close the gate."

Just as important as a foal's training is its early diet and nutrition. While a deficiency in any of the essential vitamins, amino acids, or minerals can cause a long-term problem, so too can an excess. In recent years, for example, a number of breeders and pinhookers have fed their young horses extra calcium because they've wanted them to look physically more mature for the weanling and yearling sales. The problem, according to an extensive study conducted on horses running in New York by Dr. Lennart Crook, is that while extra calcium encourages quicker bone growth, the resulting bone does not always harden completely. Pockets and cysts can form in the bones that are still cartilage, which could lead to stress fractures and other bone injuries.

John Sosby took exception to not only the mega-calcium but also the mega-vitamin approach in general. "Here we feed our horses according to their natural stage of growth," he emphasized. "The University of Kentucky has told us that the feed we use is fine from day one. It's a glorified sweet feed that Dr. John Baker came up with on the basis of twenty years of study on horse nutrition and is manufactured by Farmer's Feed Mill in Lexington."

"We use a 16 percent protein sweet feed with our yearlings and young horses and a 14 percent feed with our stallions and brood-mares," John said. "We start the foal on it when he's with his mother and continue with it when he's weaned. Years ago the feed changed when a horse was weaned. We don't do that anymore. From the day he's ready to eat grain, whether that's two weeks or a month, he won't change from that grain pattern as long as he's at Claiborne."

Because foals have soft teeth when they are born, it generally takes them at least a week before they begin to nibble on the grain. Claiborne doesn't pressure its foals, but allows them to increase their consumption of grain naturally. Depending on the individual, each mare is fastened up and their foal is given its first full quart of feed somewhere between sixty and seventy-five days after its birth. "Hope-fully, by that time," John reflected, "the foal is ready to be weaned from its mama's milk. He's already been eating clover hay, grass in the summer, and regular rations of the protein feed, and there's really not much of a dietary change. You can sometimes tell when there's been a dramatic change in the feed pattern of a horse by looking at its hoof. You'll see a ring there. A ring can also mean a horse had a temperature and was sick and maybe went off his feed for that reason."

Claiborne used to have its own men mix the protein feed. But the process proved unreliable because each man would mix in different proportions. "One guy would do twelve ounces of oats and four of bran." John shook his head. "And another would scoop up too much cracked corn. Now, with the premixed feed, if a man can count cups, we have a controlled, balanced ration. The amount of grain, of course, that each horse is fed can vary depending on the time of year and condition of the horse."

Besides grain, Claiborne horses are also fed between fourteen and eighteen pounds of first-cut clover hay each day. "We're strictly clover hay people," John emphasized. "Except in the winter months we do set aside a few tons of alfalfa for when it gets real cold and the grass has lost its nutritional value. That's when we'll throw a flake or two of alfalfa to them while they're out in the fields."

Claiborne's preference for clover hay interested me. "We're partial to clover hay because of tradition." John tapped into an important part of the farm's philosophy. "It's been producing good horses, so why change? Now, I'm not knocking any other hay. Alfalfa is a good hay, timothy is a good hay. Traditionally, we've been clover people and were very fortunate to regularly get it from Ohio and Michigan. The weather here in Kentucky just will not let you cure good clover hay. Most of the hay people in Kentucky are primarily tobacco farmers. Usually when the first cut in clover is ready to cut, they're fooling with tobacco or cattle and the clover will get too big, too stemmy, or too weedy. Whereas the people up in Ohio and Michigan are strictly hay people, and when the hay is ripe they put it up right away. We're also very fortunate in that Kentucky is centrally located, both with respect to our suppliers and the transportation network. The truckers that come in here know what we want and that we'll pay the top dollar for it. They also bring us wheat straw bedding for our mares and rye straw for our stallions."

John Sosby's last sentence intrigued me. Why would Claiborne care whether its mares were bedded down in wheat straw or rye straw? "It's based on the old wives' tale that if you put a foalin' mare on rye she'll slip her foal. Now, I don't know that to be true." John paused midway between science and folklore. "But I damn sure ain't gonna test it. I'll just take their word and use combined wheat for the mares and doe stage, cut rye for our stallions and yearlings. The rye straw is longer-stemmed than the wheat. It's usually between fifteen and eighteen inches long and has been bleached for eight to ten days. I think it's beautiful."

Apart from their gradual acclimation to a grain diet and following the lead of their human handlers, Claiborne foals live a relatively free and uncomplicated life from the time they are born until they are weaned on the first Tuesday in October. On that day, however, things change dramatically for the 187 foals that remain on the farm. "On weaning day here," John Sosby raised his intensity level up a notch, "it takes about eighty people to do the job. It's a shock for the weanlings for a day or two because Mama's not there anymore. Everybody on the farm gets involved with weaning and they all know what part they're gonna play. It's all been planned. If you're not here on weaning day, when you're on that list, you better be laying at the Bourbon County hospital or at the funeral home. There's no exception. If I don't need you on that day, I don't need you the day after either."

John emphasized the continuous care that has been taken with each foal to prepare it for weaning day. "Now remember, the first ten days of that foal's life he and his mama are put into a paddock just by themselves. That's to protect that young foal from running behind the wrong mare and getting his head kicked in or injured. Mares are very protective of their own but can be mean to other foals. We've also been training that young foal. From day one he's been haltered and led to and from his individual paddock with his mama. And then on the eleventh day he's put into a larger field with ten or twelve other mares and foals. By then he knows who his mama is."

Besides being transferred to a larger field, each foal and dam are also assigned to a new barn on the eleventh day where they will remain until the foal is weaned. Typically, the foals will be more or less of the same age and become buddies over the next five to eight months. John continued to emphasize the psychological element. "All this has been planned to ease the stress, so that every foal has a buddy, hopefully four or five, going with him on weaning day."

Okay, so what happens when 187 foals are weaned at the same time? Do they whinny, nicker, and bawl? Try to kick the shit out of the help or what? "Mama's nickering, he could be nickering or kicking," John acknowledged. "It all depends on where the sign is."

The sign? At Claiborne Farm in the twentieth century? It interested me that John Sosby still had enough druid in him to slip the lab coat of modern scientific management off and sneak a look at the evening sky. He, of course, is not alone. Lots of farmers still follow the twenty-eight-day lunar cycle, read their almanacs, and at least partly make their decisions according to the twelve signs of the zodiac, or "zone of the animals." Over eons, they will tell you, successful farmers have observed the movement of the moon in the sky relative to the movement of the constellations and identified the most propitious time for certain tasks. Some of the practices that are still followed include weaning in the sign of Capricorn, or the sign of the knees; castrating livestock in Pisces, or the sign of the feet; and cutting hay fourteen days after the full moon because of the belief that it will cure better if harvested then.

"People don't believe in the sign of the zodiac"—John paused to check my credulity—"but it works. The first Tuesday of October that sign is usually going down the leg at the knee or lower. That's tradition. Just like clover hay is tradition and wheat and rye straw are traditions. These are all traditions that we carry on."

Okay, given that the moon and the stars are right in the heavens, what happens when the foals are ready to be loaded into those vans? John explained the process. "When we get ready to load, we call out each foal by its mare's name. One of the men will be told, for example, 'Go get Flippers's foal.' So that man will go in the stall and put the shank on and when he's called out by the foreman he'll bring Flippers's foal out where five guys will be waiting. One guy will tail the foal. Two guys will get up right under his girth and lock hands. Two more guys will get on the back and then they'll all just pick the foal up and pack him right into that van. Ninety-five percent of the foals are no trouble. Five percent you don't know what they're gonna do. They might kick out or turn upside down. But once we got him on the van, we've weaned him!"

Considering that some of the foals can be as much as nine months old by early October, I wondered how big a horse we were talking about loading into the vans. "Anywhere from 470 to 700 pounds." John flexed his biceps. "So your January and February foals, those rascals have got some size on them."

And, no doubt, some kick, too. I was beginning to appreciate why some of the men, contemplating their bruises, might prefer to be absent on weaning day. Rather than having six guys pick up each foal, why doesn't Claiborne use a ramp and simply walk each foal into the van? "We have a ramp, but they won't go up on their own." John explained the farm's predicament. "They say, Whoa, what's this, Jack? and balk. That's why we have to have six guys loading. But loading them into these enclosed vans is good conditioning for later when they'll get loaded and shipped out to the various training centers."

The farm's ultimate goal, of course, is to raise a calm, athletic horse and avoid anything that will make it nervous and hard to handle later on. "Horses are creatures of habit and more comfortable with what's familiar," John reiterated. "That's why we've got Flippers's foal and a few of his buddies on that van. We *never* wean a foal by itself. We use the buddy system to keep our young horses calm. At Claiborne on weaning day there'll always be somebody in that same weaning group that's been with that foal since day eleven. From day eleven, we segregate our foals by age. We keep January with January and May with May foals. We never mismatch and put a January foal with a May foal. Then on weaning day we segregate them by sex. We put the colts with the colts and the fillies with the fillies."

Once the five or six weanlings have been loaded into the vans, most of them are shipped across town to Raceland where they will be given a preassigned stall and then raised together in groups of twelve for the rest of their weanling year and a good part of their yearling one.

John Sosby elaborated on the weanlings' initiation. "The next morning, we'll have our twelve-man crew go into those Raceland barns. And each man will go into a stall, slide the door up to where the horse can't get out, and proceed to talk to his horse. Hopefully, this horse has been handled enough that he trusts us, won't be spooked, and will then lead without any trouble."

Considering that the weanlings have been shipped across town to an unfamiliar location, just spent their first night without their mamas, and have new human handlers, I wondered if at least some of them might be a little skittish or pissed off. "I've had some weanlings that have raised a hundred dollars' worth of hell," John acknowledged. "But I've had a lot more of them where the sign was good and they didn't even nicker. Basically, we have those twelve men lead those weanlings out of their new stalls and through the gate, turn them and take them down the line, and get ready to turn them all loose. And as they go through the gate you have each man take the shank off of his horse so, if it acts up or gets away, it won't be running with the shank dangling on him and get scared and run into a fence. Because we've had that happen."

John's last comment was a reminder that the same fear/flight mechanism that evolutionarily has served the horse so well can suddenly turn suicidal in a field lined with fences. Nothing is more disheartening on a breeding farm than to see a valuable young horse spook and destroy itself against a gate or fence. At Claiborne that injured weanling might be a potential million-dollar horse, a Mr.

Prospector foal that cost somebody a $200,000 stud fee and is out of a million-dollar mare.

"Every mistake that's made could cost the farm or a client a lot of money," John agreed. "Yearlings will get into more problems than kids. They'll chew on each other's manes and tails, dig holes, crib on the fence. They'll do things you don't want them to. That's the nature of the animal we fool with. We try and teach them as many good habits as we can because a horse is a creature of habits. And they'll learn enough bad habits without us teaching them any. So it's very important how you handle them, and trust is still the key."

As fond as he is of it, John Sosby also emphasized that the farm isn't blinded by tradition. "We've learned from experience that there's an easier way to do some things than what we did thirty years ago. That's why we halter our foals from day one now, instead of waiting a week to lead him by which time he's man shy. It just improved everything we were doing because this foal had trust in that man that he wasn't gonna hurt him."

In any event, once the young horses have been weaned and let loose on their first day at Raceland, their initial response is to tentatively sniff and snort and then break as a unit into a jog through the field. But the real fun begins about four hours later when some twenty-five men enter the seventy-acre fields and try to round up the weanlings. "What you do is find a good corner to herd the horses into." John explained the most efficient approach. "Usually it's the one closest to the gate, the way our fields are designed. But first you have to block your other corners off. And then you nudge the weanlings into that good corner. You do it nice and easy and get 'em in a tight group and then send someone in there to catch them without jerking and snatching and having a rodeo-type thing, which we used to do."

Based on his thirty-five years of experience working with young horses, John Sosby clearly takes a dim view of a macho, cowboy approach. "They've got some hardboots at the racetrack." He shook his head. "I won't say they're the scum of the horse industry, but you've got some people on that racetrack that could not work here. And besides, after you reach twenty-seven or -eight years old, the old bones hurt a lot worse than when you were eighteen or nineteen. So, if you have any brains, you look for better ways, and the better ways are like we're doin' now."

Once the weanlings have been caught, they are brought back to their stalls in the reverse order they were turned out. If a horse was first going out, it'll be last going in because the farm doesn't want to condition a horse to always be a straggler or a follower. "Then you return that weanling to the same stall where he'll be until you're ready to break him. And you watch him grow. You continue to do the right things. Not only lookin' at him twice a day when you turn him out and put him up, but also when he's in his stall. Your night man is also lookin' at him four times a night as well as feedin' him some hay at nine. Depending on their breeding, each horse is a little different. And the fillies are just like little girls and the colts are like rough boys. You turn them loose and they start to fighting and a-running. And as the colts get older, they get rougher."

By the following spring Claiborne and its clients have decided which, if any, of the yearlings will be prepped for the premier auction in the world, the Keeneland July Select Yearling Sale. "Now we've chosen yearlings for that sale," John explained, "based on their pedigree and how they look. A true horseman knows what he's got. Seth Hancock knows exactly what he's got. There's no mickey-mousing with him. He knows when he has a Summer Sale–quality horse, with both pedigree and conformation. He knows which horses belong in the September Sale and which ones are gonna be broken and sent to a trainer to race."

Once Claiborne has chosen which yearlings it wants to make eligible for the July Select Sale, the sales company sends out its men to look at the horses. If they agree with Claiborne's assessment, then those horses are separated from the rest of the yearling crop, put into individual paddocks, and intensively groomed for the next hundred days.

"I like to think of the process as a football field"—John reached for a familiar metaphor—"where we start out on our one-yard line on the first day and each day we go a yard, and sale day is the hundredth day and the goal line. And it works out great that way."

Unlike a number of commercial breeders, Claiborne doesn't believe in pushing its Summer Sale yearlings. "We're not cramming anything into these horses," John emphasized. "They're not getting any drugs, steroids, that kind of thing. They're gettin' hay and feed and good water and good grass the couple of hours a day that they're gonna be out. They're down to three hours of exercise a day because we don't want to see them get hurt. They're too valuable. The last ten or twelve days before the sale they don't go out anymore. But we walk them in the mornin'. We get there at six, when the birds haven't gotten up yet, and walk them during the cool of the July mornin'. And we're groomin' on them, we're groomin' on them, and we're groomin' on them. And we've got this horse on our textured protein feed and hay. The finish is there. We might step him up from the eight or nine quarts, but we're not gonna change his eatin' habits. We've got him to the goal line, he's inside that five-yard line. We're gonna score. We're gonna sell that Mr. Prospector colt for a million or two million dollars."

Unless, of course, fate or Mother Nature fickly intervenes. When it comes to raising horses, the two things that worry John Sosby the most, apart from injuries, are barn fires and lightning storms. "Lightning we don't have any control over. But fires we try to prevent. There's no smoking in or around any of our barns. We have fire extinguishers, but there's no way they can put out a barnful of hay that's on fire."

Claiborne's worst fire in recent years was an electrical one that ignited on March 13, 1967. "It wasn't even a Friday." John tried to fathom the bad luck. "A bolt of lightning ran right up the electrical line and lit up the barn, which was a wooden structure. Eighteen yearlings died, and there was nothin' we could do but stand there helpless."

Horses generally don't try to escape from a fire, and I wondered if John had an explanation. "You tell me," he responded, totally mystified. "It's just their nature. Usually if they're free, they'll actually run right back into the fire. I don't know why. We've been very fortunate, knock on wood, over the years given the number of acres and barns that we have that we haven't had more fires."

Lightning, of course, doesn't just start barn fires. It can also hit horses while they're out in the fields. "When we get hit with a July storm and we've got seven hundred head out there, the first thing we do is go get those stallions," John Sosby emphasized. "With the rest we're more or less at the mercy of the good Lord and Mother Nature.

You can't round up seven hundred horses in the middle of a lightning storm. Hopefully, when the dust is settled and the storm is gone, everybody is still on their feet. But we've found them when they weren't."

So what happens when lightning kills horses? Does it hit them directly? Are they near trees? Doc Kaufman, whose job it is to check on them, later told me that "Sometimes it does hit them directly. Other times they'll be running and it will hit the ground and kill four or five. So it doesn't necessarily have anything to do with trees. We have lots of localized thunderstorms in the summer where there will be lightning one place and it will be clear two miles away. Almost like tornadoes. So, it just happens and there's nothing you can do about it. If we're lucky sometimes the horses are only stunned."

Though some freak injuries are unavoidable, such as from lightning or when a yearling spooks and runs into a fence or closed gate, others are preventable. As part of their daily work Claiborne employees are constantly on the lookout for fallen tree limbs and try to quickly fill in any holes the horses might have dug. Both are important to keep an exuberant yearling from stumbling, taking a misstep, and perhaps fatally snapping a front leg.

By midsummer the hundred or so yearlings that haven't been sold or shipped off to other farms are ready for the next step of their training at Claiborne. They've been weaned and acclimated to human handling, and now it's time for them to learn to accept the saddle and weight on their backs, to be gradually broken. "I go out and look for the best possible exercise people I can get, males or females." John explained the first stage of the process. "Hopefully, they've been here before. I do have the choice. We're gonna pay them the top dollar. We're gonna ride six days a week unless the horse is sick or has some kind of injury. And each of these exercise riders is gonna average between 110 to 135 pounds. I want an exercise rider with the right seat on him, where he balances his weight, so he's not gonna hurt my horse. I don't want a 170-pound guy on them. I do not ride horses. I've never rode horses. But I can tell you from the ground up how I want that yearling broke."

Once the exercise riders have been recruited, the breaking process begins in the familiarity of the yearling's twelve-by-twelve stall. "What we want is good hands." John stressed the importance of experience and safety. "We're not Allstate, but it's the same philosophy. We're gonna move into that stall and take out that water bucket, feed tub, or anything else that yearling might get tied up with or jump into. Hopefully, he's not gonna jump. But you don't know that. And not knowing that means you remove everything that horse might get tangled up with in that stall."

Next, in the reassuring presence of the groom who has been taking care of the horse for the past ten months, the exercise person approaches the yearling with a saddle pad and a surcingle, which is essentially a cinch strap. "And you gently lay that saddle pad over him," John almost whispered, "and you take that surcingle and ease it down the other side. Now the horse may be just a little skittish because it's the first time he's had a cinch around him. So you're gonna pull it up snug, but not too tight. And then the exercise person is gonna leave the stall and the groom is gonna turn that yearling. If he has any jump or buck in him, we're gonna get it out of him. If he hasn't, we're gonna reach down and tighten that cinch up another notch, but we're not gonna pinch him or scare him. Again, this is all a teaching process. We're gonna walk him right to left and left to right. Then we'll stop him, and the exercise person is gonna move back into the stall and he'll turn that yearling one more time. He's gonna pet the horse on the back and then he's gonna belly across this yearling. Now, we're gonna turn him a couple of times and if he don't do anything, we'll go ahead and straddle him that first day. But we're only gonna fool with him for maybe four or five minutes, no more. We're not gonna get him sour by overdoin' it on that first day."

The same procedure is repeated on the second day. In addition, the farm brings in a dentist to check for and remove the two vestigial "wolf teeth" that sometimes sharply protrude from a yearling's upper jaw just in front of its premolars. The dentist also *floats*, or knocks, the rough edges off the horse's teeth so that once the bridle is inserted, it won't cause any gum irritation or chafing that will cut the inside of the yearling's mouth. The dental work is intended to protect not only the horse but also the hands of the men who handle it.

On the third day, still within the confines of its stall, each yearling is introduced to the bridle and the saddle. The bridle is not entirely new because the young fillies and colts have already been led to and from the fields with a Chefney bit ever since they were weaned. Still, sensitive bridle work, especially when removing a bit from a yearling's mouth, is extremely important. "When you take that bridle out," John Sosby emphasized, "the throat latch should be undone and the cheek strap let out as far as you can so that the bit just falls out of that yearlin's mouth. You don't jerk that bridle off, you *lift* it off. That bridle is the most important piece of equipment you ever put on or take off a horse. You have to have a steering wheel to guide a horse with, and that bridle is it."

Invariably, some yearlings, just like children, will be recalcitrant. It is extremely important for members of the breaking crew to not lose their temper or patience. "If my horse gives you trouble, I *don't* want you to hit him on the head," John admonished me as he would his crew. "If you have to hit him, hit him on that rump back there, not on his head or around his eye. I don't want a man to screw up fifteen months of work on a horse with five seconds of bad behavior by jerking a bridle out of my horse's mouth or hitting him on the head. Our clients have paid good money to get these yearlin's broken and they've trusted us with these young horses and they're gonna get their money's worth, hopefully beyond their money's worth."

Once the bridle, saddle, and stirrups have been put on, and the exercise rider is up, the yearling is gradually weaned from its groom and given a *mouth*. "We're not rushing, we're not goin' to the October races at Keeneland," John stressed. "The groom is gonna take his shank off the halter and the rider is gonna be on his own. He's gonna urge and turn that yearling and then, if everything is all right, the groom is gonna step outside the stall. But he'll stay real close so, if that horse falls down, flips, or gets excited, he can run back in there to help that exercise person. At this point the rider is gonna figure-eight 'em in the stall. We're gonna put a mouth on the horse. We're gonna teach him to be led and turned by the pressure of the bridle and reins on his mouth."

John elaborated on why Claiborne initially trains its yearlings within their stalls. "It works a lot better than starting them off in a bullring or a pasture. They're not ready for that yet. We prefer to give them that seven or eight days inside their stalls first where we're gradually getting on and off that yearling, petting him on the rump, rubbing him up on the neck and on his ears, and sponging him. You want to gentle that horse because the way they're bred, they're bred to be high-strung. What we're trying to do is corral or tame whatever wildness they might have. Hopefully, there's none there."

Once the yearlings have accepted the saddle and been given a mouth, they are put into one of Claiborne's yellow vans and shipped from Raceland back to the main farm next to the half-mile training track where they will soon be jogging. At this point the farm separates its best horses. The top twenty-three yearlings are put up in the actual training barn next to the track, while the remaining seventy-two are assigned to nearby barns that earlier in the year served as foaling barns. After all the yearlings have been fed, they are turned out into adjacent fields later that afternoon and left out for the night. Given the stress of the move, the feeling is that the yearlings should be allowed to acclimate to their new surroundings before being trained further.

The next morning, however, everything gears back up. Two crews are involved. The groom crew comes in at six, puts the yearlings up, and feeds them so they have eaten by the time the second, or training, crew arrives at seven. The training crew consists of thirty-eight people and includes riders, tackers, and hot-walkers plus all the necessary equipment.

"It takes them about four hours to work through those ninety-five head of horses," John explained. "What we do is send the yearlings from the two converted foaling barns to the training center in shifts. So as one group is brought back, another is ready to move out. I have a 'dummy sheet' posted in each barn so the tacker will know which horses to get up in the sequence. Just like we have a sheet in the breeding shed telling which mare is gonna be bred to which stallion. If you're organized, it makes things go a lot better. In fact, it makes things go damn near perfect."

Well, almost. A thought troubled me. Since I knew Claiborne had started the previous year with 187 weanlings and only 95 remained, I wondered what had happened to the others. While some had been sold or shipped out to their owners, what about the rest? Had they simply been weeded out because of conformation problems and the farm's belief that they were unlikely to make good racehorses?

"No, you really don't know which ones will be the good race-horses," John responded. "So we don't weed many out on that basis. But, say we have a horse that got injured. He split a hoof or he's lame or he was a late foal and didn't develop as quick. Those we'll wait on. We'll move them into the training center in September after we've shipped some of the yearlings that belong to Howard Keck to Califor-nia, where he prefers to train them. That will open up some training stalls here for those tardy yearlings to move into."

In any event, on their second day at the training barn, the top ninety-five yearlings are once again patiently taught a new set of lessons. Each horse is first led once around the shedrow by its groom before the exercise person is allowed to mount the first one in the presence of a lead pony. "We have a lead pony named Spike," John said, "that Ewell Rice, our yearling foreman, rides just in case we need some extra assistance. Spike is just like Sea Cadet in that he doesn't have a tail. Now, that pony looks like a little fat horse, but he's worth his oats in gold to us. We've called him a little bit of everything, but he gets the job done. We love him. We did it for years without that pony, and now as I look back I don't know how we did it."

Once the yearlings have been mounted, each groom next unclips his shank and lets the rider and the horse stand on their own in an open space for the first time. Since the yearlings have never been mounted in an open space before, some of them will spook. The great majority, however, are trusting and go along with the program. "As-suming everything is going all right," John explained, "we might walk and we might jog that yearling a couple of turns the first day. A couple of turns in our training barn is probably about a sixteenth of a mile. So we've probably traveled three hundred feet overall inside the shedrow on the second day. And that's it."

On the third day, the process is reversed. The yearlings have been ridden counterclockwise for the first two days, and now they are stopped and turned in a clockwise direction. And then they learn to stand. "If a man wants to walk around one of our yearlings," John emphasized, "he can walk around one of them. We teach them to stand. Those are manners. We've had trainers come here and say, 'Hell, you must have tranquilized them.' No, these horses have been handled right. We take pride in that, that our yearlings are the best-broke yearlings in the country. He might not be the fastest horse, but he's the best broke. And if he isn't I want to know the reason why."

For eight days the same procedures are patiently repeated within the confines of the shedrow. "And that shedrow is just like Keeneland's, or any racetrack, except we have sand on the ground," John said. "And everything's done in an orderly manner, it's not every man for himself. If you start first, unless you got problems, you stay first. If there's a problem Ewell Rice will ease on up with that pony and go along with a yearling to build its confidence."

From there the yearlings are taken out to Claiborne's training track, where they're put through their finishing paces. A mixture of 60 percent sand and 40 percent topsoil, the track was originally built in 1975 after the farm tired of the daily hassle and expense of shipping some ninety-five yearlings to a rental track that was nearly eight miles away. "Our training track is basically a country track," John explained unapologetically. "It's not graded level, but rises and falls in various places. Some horse people believe that having a horse gallop uphill and downhill develops all of their muscles better than a uniformly level surface. And, of course, each June we add soil amendments and recondition the track because it's been been dormant since the previous November and washed out some by the rain."

The track also has a three-stall starting gate that is used for training purposes only. "The horses are never broken out of it like in a real race," John emphasized. "The first day they come here they just walk through that gate. Later we stand them in there to get them used to that feeling. Once they're out on the track, we walk, jog, and gallop them—then reverse the order and gallop, jog, and walk them around this half-mile track. We alternate them clockwise one day and then counterclockwise the next, so they get used to changing both leads. Even at the end we still work them slow. We never get them to the breezing stage, never ask them for speed. What we're trying to do is put a good foundation under them, but leave the breezing to the trainer when he gets them."

The training process that began in late July concludes on the last Saturday in October when the fall rains come and the training track gets too muddy to safely work the horses on anymore. Instead the yearlings, some of which are approaching two, are turned out for the last three weeks of their stay at Claiborne. "Now, not everybody agrees with turning horses out like we do," John Sosby acknowledged. "You ask ten people, you get ten different answers. But we like to rest them then. If they're decent racehorses, they're not gonna get a break again. They're gonna be a racehorse until the end of their career."

From mid-November on, the broken yearlings are shipped south to winter training centers where it's up to a new set of horsemen to make successful racehorses out of them. By then trainers like Shug McGaughey, Bill Mott, and Steve Penrod have shifted their base from the New York and Kentucky tracks down to South Carolina and Florida. The majority of Claiborne's yearlings will go to training centers in Camden or Aiken in South Carolina, though some go to Florida and a few, such as those owned by Howard Keck, have already gone to Cardiff Stud Farm in California. "Now it's up to the trainers"—John passed the baton—"and we hope these reports that start coming back around the first of April or May say, 'Got one that can fly!' 'Got a Forty Niner that would knock your eyes out.' That's what we're waiting for."

Like everything else in horse racing, John Sosby agreed, predicting which yearlings are destined to become real athletes remains mostly an enigma. "The Moccasins, the Buckpassers, the Ruffians, the Easy Goers. Yes, we can generally tell. They've got pedigree and we've been watching their action. The Swales, the Forty Niners, maybe. We knew they were there, we liked them. But, as far as being what they turned out to be, I'd be lying to you if I said yes, I picked them all. I haven't. But if Flippers had a three-legged horse, I'd have to like him anyway because Moccasin was her mother and she's my all-time favorite mare. Moccasin was two-year-old filly champion and Horse of the Year. She foaled seven stakes winners and a champion. And now I'm really partial to her because Flippers has a two-year-old named Sosby by Private Account!"

"A two-year-old named Sosby? How'd he get a name like that?" I teased John, fully aware of the appreciation Seth Hancock has for the job he does.

"I touted him and touted him." John beamed. "Frank Whitley has him at Camden right now and Shug McGaughey will get him at the racetrack in New York sometime in April or May. What happened was that we got him in the breakdown with Mr. Perry last July. I told Seth, 'We get this horse, send him to a good trainer.' Then, when Seth came out of the meeting with Mr. Perry, he joshed me around a little and said, 'I took the Forty Niner rather than the Flippers colt.' So I said, 'Well, that's all right. I still like Flippers's colt.' And Seth had a big old grin on his face and said, 'No, I got him. Tell you what, we'll send him to Shug.' And I said, 'Okay, we're battin' a thousand!' And then Seth said, 'You know we like short five-letter names. How many letters in your last name?' I said, 'Five. . . . No, Seth.' He said, 'Yeah. We'll name him Sosby.' And he turned to Annette Couvalt and said, 'Name the Flippers colt Sosby.' They submitted the name and we had a little static on it. I thought, There can't be another Sosby. Anyhow they approved the name, then Seth kidded me some more and said he was going through Keeneland in September. Recently somebody asked, 'How's Sosby doing?' And Seth said, 'John's fine.' And they said, 'No, I'm talking about the horse.' Anyhow, since he's got my name, I hope he can run. And, if he can't, I asked Seth never to castrate him." (Sosby broke his maiden at Aqueduct.)

Once the yearlings have been shipped to the racetrack, the farm hopes they will continue to develop. Besides a good pedigree and conformation, I wondered how important John Sosby thought a yearling's temperament is as an indication of possible future success. "The toughest, most aggressive yearlings don't always make the best racehorses," he reflected, "but it's a good sign. I'd rather have one, not a bully or a rogue, but a horse that wants to be out front, that wants to be the leader. I don't know if a horse runs faster because they're scared or want to be superior. You can train them to do various things, but some of them are born to run. Some are bred to run. Others are just born. Some horses will develop no matter what the trainer does to them. Does a trainer make a horse or the horse a trainer? I don't know. But, just like I'll tell any trainer that I'm the farm manager here and don't tell me how to farm, I don't tell the trainer how to train."

12

RACELAND

*T*he next morning around six-thirty I met up with Ewell Rice, the yearling manager, at Louie's restaurant on the Claiborne side of Paris. Louie's is a down-home hangout for local horse people where, at any given time, you're likely to bump into everyone, from a farrier like Wick Stone eating a cheeseburger and complaining about his taxes, to Seth or Arthur Hancock quietly talking horses with a client in one of the corners. In addition, with a big assist from Louie's irreverent and dramatic wife, Ruby, it's a great place to catch up on all the latest gossip.

Ruby, of course, also preserves some semblance of order and is no doubt responsible for the sign UNATTENDED CHILDREN WILL BE SOLD INTO SLAVERY, which greets any potentially backsliding or permissive parent who enters the premises. Originally from upstate New York, Ruby enjoys kidding any visitor bold enough to ask how she came to live in Paris, saying she was snatched from the Empire State and brought to Kentucky under false pretenses. "When Louie promised to take me to Paris," she'll say, feigning innocence, "I thought he meant France."

In addition to Ruby's wit, the food at Louie's is ample and satisfying. For breakfast a hungry body can order anything from grits and eggs, to biscuits and gravy with a side order of pork chops or ham thrown in. The dinner menu includes Kentucky fried chicken, steak, spaghetti and meatballs, and even chimichangas, a chicken or beef burrito dish flavored with chiles and a special sauce. You also can spice your palate with a cold beer, a glass of wine, or a dry martini while gazing at the signed portrait of Waylon Jennings (he liked the bean soup) that hangs from one wall or the large framed photos of Swale (1984) and Sunday Silence (1988) winning the Kentucky Derby for the Hancock brothers that grace two others.

Ewell Rice, for his part, had already finished breakfast and was hunched over his coffee reading the local paper. A sandy-complexioned man who wears his nearly seventy years with ease, Ewell speaks with a dry, almost western accent that sounded more like Kansas or the Texas Panhandle than Kentucky to me. Once Ruby had called out my order for grits and eggs, Ewell somberly told me that our plans for later that morning had been changed because of an emergency on the farm. Gus Koch's dad, the turf writer Charles Koch, was in the hospital in critical condition, and Gus had left to maintain a round-the-clock vigil. To help out, Ewell had volunteered to pinch-hit for Gus with the broodmares and arranged for Wayne Clem to give me a tour of the Raceland yearling operation in his place.

After taking a hit of my coffee, I steered our conversation away from the gravity of Gus's immediate situation and learned that Ewell grew up on a farm where Lane's End now stands. His initial interest in horses, he told me, was quite practical. Like most schoolboys, he hated to walk. So he and his friends took to hopping over a neighbor's fence, jumping bareback on his horses, and then riding to where the school bus picked them up. "Most of the horses in those days," Ewell reminisced, "weren't haltered and we'd hop on the closest one to us and ride from one end of a hundred-acre field to the other."

After leaving school, Ewell didn't wander far. He subsequently put in forty-one years at Calumet Farm before coming to Claiborne in 1983. While at Calumet he helped raise horses like Tim Tam, General Duke, and Alydar. I asked Ewell if there was anything special about Alydar as a yearling. "Yes, indeed. I remember a photographer that came to Calumet and told me he wanted me to pick out three yearlings that he could follow that would likely be good three-year-olds. I told him he only needed one and that was Alydar. Because *there* was a chestnut colt that, if you looked out at him in a field, stood out. Everything I did with him, he stood out. As a yearling he was very sensible and easy to work with. He was a leader. He could outwalk or outrun anything in the field. Of course, a horse like that doesn't always become a runner at the racetrack. But Alydar did it so easy and did it the right way that you could tell he was something special. He would take those long even, confident strides—rather than short choppy strides—that are the mark of a good horse when he's walking out in a field or being led."

What about Ewell's experience at Claiborne with Easy Goer and Forty Niner? Did they have that same star quality as yearlings? "Easy Goer was kind of like that. He did everything easy, nothing bothered him. Forty Niner didn't stand out as much as a yearling. I wouldn't have picked him to go on like he did. Of course, I was only taking care of thirty yearlings at Calumet, and it's harder to pick out the best one when you have over a hundred like we have at Claiborne."

Ewell's role with the lead pony while Claiborne's yearlings are being broken interested me. "With the numbers that we have here," he explained, "you're gonna find a few yearlings that are a little bit nervous, that shy away from the rider on another horse next to them because that's something they haven't seen before. With the pony next to him the nervous horse will settle down and relax and follow the others in a line in what we call a duck style. Usually you'll find one yearling in each group that's a leader, and the rest will follow."

Some horses, however, get so nervous they spook during the breaking process. "Discover was that kind of yearling," Ewell recalled with an amused grin. "He was one that would be walking along and then suddenly jump straight up four feet in the air just like a deer. So I put the pony beside him until he realized that he didn't have to jump, that he could do what the other horses were doing. After a couple of days, he was walking all right. The pony is also helpful in getting the yearlings to learn to turn, because initially they don't want to turn. But the thing that spooks them most is when the wind breaks a branch or blows a limb across a field. Any sudden movement or noise like a truck or a car backfiring will spook them. Thunder they get used to pretty quickly. But something out of the normal routine, that's when they do strange things and can hurt themselves."

Ewell drained the last of his coffee, placed the mug on the table, and said it was time to get to work. But before he left I couldn't resist asking him, on the basis of his fifty years of experience, what his best advice was to anyone crazy enough to plunge into the breeding side of the sport. "What you want to do is start off with a filly," he counseled, "because you have two shots to make it with. She may be a good racehorse, but even if she's not a great racehorse she can still make a good broodmare. Whereas if a colt can't run, you ain't got nothing. I knew a guy who got into the horse business and was three for three with fillies and went out and bought nine colts and struck out with all of them. So starting with fillies is really where it's at."

Forty-five minutes later I was out at the Raceland facility with Wayne Clem, who is the yearling foreman there. A short, stocky, deliberative man in his late thirties, Clem speaks with a languid, rural accent that makes him seem more taciturn than he really is. He was driving a Claiborne pickup with a camper shell mounted over its empty bed and explaining that his immediate objective was to round up all the grooms from the various Raceland barns so the yearlings could be turned out more efficiently in groups of ten at a time. As he talked the two-way radio inside the cab periodically interrupted our conversation with messages of one kind or another. One of the dispatches asked Doc Kaufman to get over to Raceland and check out a sick yearling.

The Raceland facility, Wayne proudly told me, consists of 632 acres and can put up to 106 head in its five barns, four of which are concrete and fireproof. "And each barn has two fields which adjoin it," he added. "So altogether we have ten fields that run sixty acres or more. We started with 104 weanlin's last October, but we lost a few. So right now we have 97 yearlin's."

Over the next fifteen minutes Wayne stopped at four of the barns, each time picking up two ruddy-cheeked grooms who hopped into the back of the camper rubbing their hands and stomping their feet. While the heater in the front cab kept Wayne and me warm as toast, the men's actions reminded me that outside the fickle February weather had turned cold once again.

The grooms hunched in the back of the truck were a varied lot. I knew from talking to John Sosby and Bobby Anderson that they occupy the basic entry-level position on the farm and are typically paired up two to a barn, with each man feeding and watering eleven yearlings, mucking their stalls, and helping to lead them to and from the fields. At night a caretaker groom makes his rounds and checks on the yearlings, topping off their water buckets as necessary.

Looking closer at the men, I saw that some were animated and cracked jokes while others, given Bourbon County's depressed economy, seemed older and were probably just happy to have a job. But one thing about them particularly struck me. Unlike the not too distant past, when most grooms would have been black, these men were all white. When I later asked Doc Kaufman about it, he told me, "Most of the young black men in this area have moved into the city and haven't grown up around horses. They don't know how to handle big animals."

Wayne pulled up in front of the fifth and last yearling barn, where all of us climbed out of the camper and joined the two grooms already there. The grooms then proceeded to the first set of stalls, which contained only young colts. While his men fanned up and down the U-shape shedrow, Wayne paused in front of the first stall and explained why all the yearlings are identified by their dams. "For instance, this here yearlin' is a 1991 Cadillacing. We couldn't say it was a 1991 Danzig after his daddy because there would be too many 1991 Danzigs to keep track of. So all the foals and yearlin's on the farm are identified by their dams."

As we continued down the shedrow I noticed that, just as in the stallion barn, a number of stalls had brass plaques, with names of famous horses inscribed on them, mounted hip high on the sliding doors. At Raceland the older plaques honor any yearling that previously occupied a particular stall that won $100,000 or more. In recent years, with the higher purse structure, the ante has been raised. A yearling now has to win a Graded Stakes before it qualifies for Claiborne's hall of fame.

Among the names that glistened in front of me in the crisp morning light were Yonder, Time for a Change, Lt. Stevens, What a Pleasure, Chief's Crown, Trucemaker, Gulch, and Bold Lad. All horses that had done Claiborne proud. Beyond honoring the horses, I reflected, each plaque is a constant reminder to the grooms that any one of the yearlings they care for might, if properly raised, develop into a champion.

Wayne paused in front of a closed stall door and pointed to a colt behind it that had some lesions on his neck and a breathing problem. He was being given stall rest by Doc Kaufman, Wayne related, because his condition might worsen if he was allowed to run with the other horses. Instead, the colt would get his daily exercise in a special isolation paddock until he was well enough to rejoin the other yearlings.

By the time we reached the last stall, each one of the ten grooms had put a shank on his yearling colt, led him outside his stall, and was awaiting further instructions. Satisfied that everything was in order, Wayne gave the command and the men led their yearlings single file out toward the nearby gate that controlled passage into an adjacent sixty-acre, fenced field. This particular parade was a smooth one except for an impatient Danzig colt that had a mind of his own. He kept trying to snatch the shank from out of his groom's right hand. "With cool weather like this," Wayne explained, "some yearlin's will act up a little more. When it's warm most of them are more deadheaded."

As soon as the Danzig colt had calmed down, Wayne signaled for the gate to be opened, and the men then sequentially turned their horses leftward into the field. Once inside, all the yearlings were attentively lined up against the fence while the gate was closed. With everything secured, Wayne shouted out, "All right," and in unison the grooms unshanked their horses, leaving them to their own proclivities.

Once free, the yearlings paused for a moment, then bolted and ran as a herd for a few yards before gradually fanning out into smaller groups with their buddies. After a couple of minutes most of the horses settled down and began to graze, though a few were more rambunctious and nipped at one another's manes and tails.

Over the past years, I learned, Claiborne has tried to dissuade its yearlings from inordinately chewing one another by applying an aloe and creosote paste to their manes and tails. More recently an unsavory mixture of red pepper and axle grease has worked even better. The farm's objective, of course, isn't to be cruel, but to have their yearlings look the part—which isn't the case if they look as if they're coming down with a bad case of the mange.

Wayne's crew repeated the turning-out process with the remaining colts on the other side of the barn, who were released into a separate adjacent field of their own. Everybody then hopped back into the camper, and we headed toward the next barn, which was full of yearling fillies. The privately paved blacktop road we traveled on was flanked on both sides by a continuous row of large, dormant maples whose leaves, come summer, would provide a deep wall of shade and, in autumn, a riot of crimson and gold. Most of the maples had been planted some thirty years earlier when Bull Hancock first bought the Raceland acreage.

As he drove, Wayne elaborated on how the yearlings are organized. "We have three barns of colts and two barns of fillies this year. You can tell the fillies because they aren't as muscled as the colts are. We also segregate them accordin' to age. The early foals are in one barn and the late ones in another. Most of these comin' up were born in January and February. Organizin' the yearlin's accordin' to age is important because otherwise the younger horses tend to be bullied by the older ones and have their confidence undermined."

When we pulled up to the filly barn, Doc Kaufman was already there. He had responded to the radio dispatch and was looking at a yearling that had mucus in her nose and was running a temperature. He applied some Vicks VapoRub, a common remedy for the snots, gave the filly some antibiotics to guard against possible pneumonia, and recommended she not be turned out for a couple of days. While Doc is always ready to deal with illness, he stressed that most of his work on the farm is preventive. Toward that end, all the horses on the farm are wormed when they are ten weeks old and every eight weeks thereafter. They are also vaccinated against tetanus and influenza in August and September of their first year.

While we waited for the grooms to bring the young fillies out of their stalls, Wayne elaborated on his foreman duties. "Basically, I watch the yearlin's and make sure everything's okay and call Doc if any of the horses look sick. Last week, for instance, this bay filly somehow got its right front foot caught up in the chin strap of her halter and reared up and had both feet on the fence and couldn't get off of it. She's sick now and Doc thinks it might be because she hurt her back on that fence."

Not the brightest of creatures, horses will trap themselves against fences when it's wet and muddy. "Sometimes they'll lay down and roll right up against the fence and get all four feet against it and can't get off," Wayne explained. "They'll just thrash against the fence and you've got to get ahold of 'em and pull 'em off. The same thing can happen in a stall where a horse will roll over and pin himself against a wall. It sounds strange but a horse that gets too close to a wall with his body, with his legs trapped in between, can't turn himself back over. You've got to go in there and grab hold of the halter and pull him away from that wall."

The danger of leaving an unattended yearling trapped against a wall is that it might panic and hurt itself. "That's right," Wayne agreed. "That's why we check the fields and have each groom check his stalls to make sure the horse is all right and has plenty of water. Same thing with the night man, who comes in at six and checks every horse on the hour for the rest of the night."

Not surprisingly, Claiborne's yearlings eat a lot. To replenish the energy they expend cavorting in those sixty-acre fields, as well as to give them something to grow on, they are fed two quarts of grain twice a day. One feeding is at seven in the morning, just before being turned out, and the next between two and three in the afternoon when they are brought back in. In addition, they also consume lots of grass and hay. "The guys that muck out the stalls for the yearlin's have more dirty work than the broodmare or stallion grooms," Wayne wryly observed. "Because the yearlin's eat more, they also shit more'n the other horses."

After the grooms have finished mucking out all the stalls, topped off the water buckets, and dispensed the feed, they still, of course, have to bring the yearlings in from the fields before they can leave. At two o'clock each afternoon the men climb back into Wayne's camper and reverse the morning process, first catching the yearlings and then putting them back into their stalls for the night. "Generally, the horses are cooperative," Wayne explained, "because they're hungry and know they have to go back through the gate before they'll be fed. On a good day, the afternoon roundup takes about forty minutes. On a bad one up to an hour and twenty minutes."

The weather, in Wayne's experience, has a lot to do with how the yearlings behave. "When it's good and warm, the horses are usually waitin' for us right by the gate ready to come in. For some reason, the cold and blustery days, like today, are the ones where we have to chase after 'em. Each of these fields is close to sixty acres, so that gives these yearlin's quite a bit of room to run around in. That helps develop their muscles and lungs, but," Wayne concluded on a comic note, "it also helps develop the muscles and coordination of my men 'cause they have to chase after 'em."

13

TOURING

*L*ater that afternoon I hooked back up with John Sosby for a tour of the rest of the farm. Our first stop was Dell Hancock's house, which is located near the half-mile training track behind the foaling barns. Dell is Seth's sister and an accomplished photographer. The animated Claiborne stallion shots that appear in the farm's *Blood-Horse* and *Thoroughbred Times* ads are part of her work. "Look at that bluebird there," John enthused as he pointed toward the back of Dell's house. "Bluebirds are good luck. Dell must have a little feeder over there. She's been gone six weeks on vacation. We used to call it the Gashouse before Dell and her dogs moved in. What you see was rebuilt from two brick houses that were originally here. We also added the patio and that pergola for those vines to climb up. Again, I love to fool with different things. Not only with breedin' horses, but all the things that go with running a farm."

John released the emergency brake and eased the Blazer back onto the paved road. As we crossed over Kennedy Creek, I asked him about the farm's water supply. "Again we're blessed because of our water," he expounded. "It percolates through that limestone and has the right minerals in it for promoting good bone. We do have one well on the farm, but Stoner Creek is our major source of water. It's spring fed and forms in the next county above us about ten miles from here. Three miles of it run through Claiborne and then it snakes its way to Paris where it becomes the town's water supply. After that it goes on to the next city and flows into the Licking River, which ultimately flows north into the Ohio River at Cincinnati."

A few minutes later we pulled up to Seth Hancock's large, colonial-style home, which is on the Marchmont section of the farm just across the road from his mother's house. "It sits on twenty-one acres and Seth don't mow a damn blade of grass," John teased.

Of course, these days John Sosby doesn't mow the several-acre lawn either, but gets one of his men to do it. As the farm division and yearling manager, he has bigger fish to fry. While the basic routine of running the farm is left up to John and his staff, he emphasized that it's the teamwork that makes things run smoothly. Particularly important are the monthly management meetings, which include Sosby, Gus Koch, Ed Boyle (the maintenance supervisor), Jim Freiss (the financial manager), and, of course, Seth Hancock.

"We all sit down, and it could be a thirty-minute meeting or a two-hour meeting." John put on his corporate hat. "We review what has happened over the past thirty days and any notes that I have about what is gonna happen during the next thirty days or even six months. Things like topping roads, building fence, putting roofs on barns and painting them. Or maybe refurbishing the stallion barn after the breeding season, putting down rubber brick roads, or mowing the grass and seeding the pastures. There's always something to do, and that's great. I can get up right now and find a hundred things to do. If the sun will pop out and dry things off, I'll find two hundred things to do. That's the nature of what we're foolin' with. But how can you be any luckier? The sun comes up, the sun shines, and man, you're ready to go, huh!"

It would be hard to find two more divergent but complementary personalities than John Sosby and Seth Hancock. One man is ebullient and loquacious, the other cautious and laconic. About their working relationship, John reflected, "Are you an optimist or a pessimist? Is the glass half full or half empty? I like to say the glass is half full. I'm an extreme optimist. Seth is an extreme pessimist. He tells me, 'I shouldn't have asked you anyway, because you're gonna say everything is gonna be all right.' Well, what other way can I feel? I think as long as I'm breathin' that everything is gonna be all right. Now, Seth thinks if it's gonna rain today, and he wanted to do something, it's the end of the world."

We moved on to Cherry Valley Farm, which was a corn farm when Seth bought it in 1977 with the idea of converting it for horses. Over the next ten years John helped add three barns, a shop, and a house to it. But by 1988 Seth concluded he didn't want the hassle of running a separate farm anymore and decided to lease the property to Claiborne instead. "It's worked out great for us," John observed, "because these are facilities we can definitely use."

A mile or so farther down the road, John stopped his Blazer in front of a man-made pond stocked with channel cats and large-mouthed bass. "They'll run up to three pounds." John smacked his lips and patted his belly. "Pretty good fishing when you get a chance to fish."

Unfortunately, John doesn't get much of a chance. When he does he takes an extremely pragmatic approach. "If I don't get a bite in ten minutes, I'm out of there." He laughed. "I'm not an impatient guy, but I want to see some action. If I don't get a bite I move on to the next job."

Next we stopped in front of Barn 20 where horses from Claiborne's racing stable convalesce from the rigors of racetrack life. Most of them are horses that have been running in the Midwest and are in need of a thirty- to sixty-day "freshening" on the farm. A few are injured horses that have shipped in from New York and California for surgery and a more extended rest. Because flying is expensive, Claiborne vans most of its horses. "Hopefully the van company has a full load and we get a better rate." John explained the economics. "That's why we tell them to send us the horse at the carrier's convenience, so they can plan a trip with a full load. We use the Sallee Van company. They're great. They don't dally around. They treat every horse just like they're the owner."

From my first day on the farm, when John excitedly informed me that a maiden filly of his had finally won a race, I'd known that he not only likes to raise horses for Claiborne, but also runs some under his own Bourbon Star Stable colors. About the killer expenses involved, John harked back to the two-year-old maiden filly that had finally won for him at Turfway. "I told you it cost $35,000 before she broke her maiden. But actually, we won $14,000 along the way, so we're only short $21,000."

It was a familiar story. I asked John if, given the harsh economic realities, he was surprised to see any racing going on, especially at the maiden claiming level. "Hell, they always said it was the rich man's sport," he replied with a twinkle in his eyes. "Years ago it was the sport of kings. They were right too."

Still, that hard knowledge hasn't stopped John Sosby (and a lot of other horse lovers) from trying to beat the game. In fact, working for Claiborne has given him a bit of an edge in that some of his brood-mares have come as gifts from the farm. These were yearling fillies with physical defects that did not fit into Seth Hancock's plans. "Since they couldn't be sold and cost money to board, Seth gave them to me," John explained. "They're two-year-old fillies now and I won't breed them until next year. It's possible that I'll get a decent horse out of them. One of them is by Forty Niner and the other by Cox's Ridge. They have good bloodlines but no conformation for various reasons. If I can compensate for their defects with the right stallion, I might get lucky."

It was time for us to head back to the main office. But, along the way, John couldn't resist the temptation of pulling over to look at half a dozen foals that were playing next to their mares. "Ah, but that's the future!" he crooned. "You've seen how we raise our horses without pampering or abusing them. We let them grow in their natural environment and be a horse. Let a kid be a kid. Because once you become an adult and start to work, there's no play anymore. So, let that kid or foal play, because once he's a racehorse, that's it. That's my philosophy and belief, and I've seen it work!"

14

CLIENT RELATIONS
AND INFORMATION
CONTROL

*I*t was nearly six and the faintly lit horizon was curving into night when I checked back with Annette Couvalt. Though the horses had been put up for the evening and most of the daytime staff had gone home, Annette was still at her desk, after a busy day on the phone, catching up on the voluminous paperwork that is part of her job. Besides booking the stallions and typing up the next day's breeding schedule, she is also responsible for registering the farm's foals with the Jockey Club. Annette intrigued me because I figured that after fourteen years at Claiborne, she had to have a unique and interesting perspective on not only the farm's client base, but also the Thoroughbred industry.

I knew, of course, that an important ingredient in Claiborne's success over the years has been the partnerships the farm has formed periodically with key clients as a way of raising capital, spreading the risk, and, best of all, sharing in the benefits. Certainly the syndications of Sir Gallahad III in 1925, Blenheim II in 1936, and Nasrullah in 1949 were three prime examples. Not only did these syndications make possible the importation of those key stallions from Europe, but they also produced horses like Gallant Fox, Whirlaway, and Bold Ruler and ensured the continued patronage of affluent individuals like banker William Woodward, retailer Marshall Field, Calumet owner Warren Wright, and several generations of the Phipps family.

Similarly, Claiborne has formed innovative partnerships to share in the cost of raising its horses and maintaining a racing stable. Paramount in this regard is the farm's long-standing arrangement with William Haggin Perry in which he owns a half interest in part of Claiborne's yearling crop.

Fascinated by the terms of this unique arrangement, I asked Annette to elaborate. "Well, Mr. Perry comes in once a year," she replied. "And he and Seth decide if there are any yearlings to be sold. By this time of year [in late February], we already know which, if any, yearlings are going to be sold because the Summer Select Sale nominations were due in January. So you have to plan ahead for that kind of thing. For all the other co-owned yearlings with Mr. Perry, who operates under the Gamely Corporation, Seth will pair yearlings. He tries to take two yearlings, usually by sex—fillies with fillies and colts with colts—he believes are of similar quality, and then he and Mr. Perry alternate in picking one each to race under the Gamely or Claiborne silks. Any purse money is split equally, regardless of whose silks the horses race under. Mr. Perry has been such a long-standing client that he's practically a member of the Claiborne family. He and Seth pretty much agree on everything."

In any event, once the horses have been divided up between the two men, they are shipped to their respective racing stables with Scotty Schulhofer and Bill Mott training for Gamely and Shug McGaughey and Steve Penrod getting most of Claiborne's horses. "Steve Penrod used to be the yearling manager here," Annette explained, "and now trains for us in the Midwest at Churchill Downs, Keeneland, and Arlington. He also takes all the Claiborne yearlings to Aiken, South Carolina, and helps get them ready for the other

Claiborne trainers. The decision of how to race Claiborne/Gamely horses, even though they are co-owned, resides with whichever stable is managing them. Still, if it happens to be a really good horse, then it's going to be pretty much mutually discussed."

Considering the huge purses in California, the absence of West Coast trainers interested me. "Well, Willard Proctor used to train for us," Annette recollected. "And Dick Mandella is taking six or seven this year for us. Most of them have just turned two. So it will be a while before we know how they do. We don't keep a lot of horses in California because Seth doesn't get out there that much to see them run."

Not surprisingly, Claiborne's office complex, like the rest of the farm, is extremely well organized. Prominently posted on several walls are pegboards that keep track of all the farm's horses. Each horse's location on the farm is identified according to the specific parcel, barn, and stall number in which it is domiciled. Pointing to a chart that listed Claiborne's current runners, I asked Annette to talk about how the farm keeps tabs on them. Like everyone else on the farm, she was particularly excited about Forty Niner because a positive performance by his first crop of two-year-olds in 1992 would validate his $60,000 stud fee and have a significant impact on the farm's future income.

"With Forty Niner's foals being two-year-olds this year," Annette said, emphasizing the homebred's importance, "Seth knows where *all* of them are at, and with which trainers. He knows a lot of people around the country that will keep their ears to the ground for him for Forty Niner. I spoke to Charlie Whittingham a couple of weeks ago, and he has a Forty Niner colt that belongs to Mr. Howard B. Keck. So I asked him to let us know, good, bad, or indifferent, what he hears about our Forty Niners."

Not all of Forty Niner's foals, of course, belong to Claiborne. They belong to whomever paid the stud fee and owns the mare. I wondered about the range of support in Forty Niner's first three books, especially how many outside mares he was bred to. "Seth bred around ten Claiborne mares to Forty Niner his first year," Annette reported. "By Seth I'm saying Claiborne and Gamely and also Cherry Valley Farm. So, outside breeders represented the bulk of the mares that were initially bred to Forty Niner."

Outside breeders typically breed by what is called a contract service. "Everything, regrettably, has to be documented on paper." Annette explained the legal mechanics. "The days of a handshake documenting a stallion season, I'm afraid, are gone. Because it has to be documented who's responsible for the Kentucky sales tax, when the fee is due, is it refundable or not refundable. With Forty Niner the contract currently stipulates that his stud fee is $60,000 live foal plus tax, payable when the foal stands and nurses. That stud fee may change depending on what happens with his first two crops."

Given the $321,000 average price that Forty Niner's first yearlings commanded at Keeneland in 1991, outside commercial breeders that had initially bred to him had to be pleased by the results. In a depressed market they had received better than a fivefold return on Forty Niner's $60,000 stud fee! Whether subsequent breeders do as well will depend on how Forty Niner's first two crops actually do once they hit the racetrack in 1992 and 1993.

Forty Niner, like most potentially valuable stallions, was insured his first year against possible infertility. Insurance companies normally insure a stallion's fertility predicated on the percent of mares in his book that conceive. Since there are always going to be some barren mares, insurance companies protect themselves by requiring that the conception rate drop below a certain percentage (usually 60 percent) before they will deem a stallion infertile and pay off on a claim. They also limit their liability by limiting a stallion's book during his first year.

"You have to have a special dispensation from them," Annette emphasized, "to breed more than fifty mares. Forty Niner bred to fifty-one mares in 1989 and I'm sure we got approval to breed that extra mare from our local Lloyd's of London agent. If you know that your stallion is stopping mares very well, and if you have in-hand pregnancy certificates on these mares, they will usually allow you to breed a few more. But Seth doesn't like to start a young horse with a lot of mares anyway."

Forty Niner, fortunately, had no fertility problems. Of the fifty-one mares that were initially bred to him, forty-six conceived. His fertility percentage of 90.2 percent was well above the industry average. "After his first year Forty Niner has been bred to more mares," Annette continued, "because there is no longer fertility insurance on him. That always expires after the first year when a stallion has demonstrated that he's fertile. Fortunately, we've never had to pay a claim."

While it's uncommon, it's not unheard of for a great racehorse to be infertile when he comes to stud. Precisionist, for example, was almost sterile and could get only one mare in foal out of an entire book. There are also certain bloodlines that are statistically less fertile than others. "The Northern Dancer bloodline, with a few notable exceptions, is not an essentially fertile bloodline," Annette stated. "The Raise a Native bloodline, on the other hand, is an extremely fertile one. Nevertheless, virtually every syndicated stallion is brought in with fertility insurance because the owners would have to refund all syndicate payments if the stallion were not fertile."

Interestingly, unlike most other farms, Claiborne doesn't do fertility tests on its stallions. Gus Koch had previously explained to me why not. "We figure, what's the purpose? What are you gonna do if the horse's sperm count is a little low? You're gonna breed him anyhow. All you're gonna do with these fertility tests is spread nasty rumors about your horse. If you check the semen and the vet says, 'Jeez, the sperm didn't live very long, there's a question here,' you know what happens? Word spreads throughout the whole horse business that there's something wrong with your horse's fertility, that he's sterile. And then everybody scratches their good mares and sends you their maiden mare or one that's been barren for several years. And it kills your horse before he's even had a chance to prove his fertility. So why do it? Our fertility insurance isn't based on testing a sample of semen and then saying 'Okay, he's fertile.' No. It's based on a whole year at stud. We breed forty-four mares to him and if he gets over 60 percent of them in foal, then he's considered a fertile horse."

Interestingly the reason Claiborne now insures its stallions on a 60 percent in-foal basis rather than on a semen test is because of what happened when Secretariat first came to stud. "Secretariat's semen was very poor quality-wise," Gus recalled. "Yet he was a very fertile horse and got his mares in foal. But because of the semen test, everybody got up in arms, even though Secretariat was very fertile. So, instead of worrying about every new stallion now, we just breed the horse for five months and see how he does. At the end of the breeding season we figure up how many mares did he get in foal. If he got 90 percent of his mares in foal, he's a fertile horse. That's a much better test than a lab test. Meanwhile, we've been paying insurance premiums on him for fertility and now we cancel it. And the insurance company has made money on us, because we paid them premiums. But if the horse only stops three mares and we bred forty mares to him, then he's not fertile and they owe us our insurance money. But they get the horse. There are a lot of wrinkles in fertility insurance though and every farm does it differently."

Still, I wondered how Seth Hancock responds to potential clients when they point out that a number of competing farms routinely do semen tests. "Well, the proof's in the pudding," he explained in his office one afternoon. "If a stallion gets his mares in foal, that's the ultimate test of fertility. If a stallion gets 90 percent of his mares in foal and averages 1.5 to 1.7 covers per mare, you can't beat that. Last year Mr. Prospector's fertility was 98 percent. Believe It was 92.5; Buckfinder, 84.8; Conquistador Cielo, 89.9; Cox's Ridge, 88.6; Danzig, 92; and Demons Begone was 97 percent. The lowest one here in 1991 was Linkage with 73 percent and he's gone."

A stallion's fertility rate, of course, has a lot to do with a well-managed teasing program, and Seth was quick to credit his staff for Claiborne's success. "Those guys you've been with in the mornings all week are absolute pros," he affirmed. "They're the best in the world, and so is Dr. Kaufman. Most all of the big farms in Kentucky have guys like that. And, as I'm sure you've seen, those teasers are important. And that son of a gun handling that teaser is even more important. You're not going to do any better than Billy Purcell and Ronnie Hunt and E. J. Caswell and Jerry Allen, the four guys we have here handling that chore. And one thing that really helps us is that our mare population basically stays the same. It's not like we have three hundred mares to fool with this year and then three hundred different ones next year. Two hundred and forty of them are going to be the same, and each of them has its own idiosyncrasies, and these guys know them and can tell when they're ready to be bred."

In any event, once a stallion has proven his fertility, most farms increase the number of mares they breed to him the following year. "Around here," Annette reported, "a big book for a young, healthy, fertile stallion is in the middle sixties. Sometimes, for a few horses, that number will creep into the low seventies. But that can be a little deceptive, because maybe those mares weren't added until June when things have begun to slow down. Some farms think seventy is a large number; others consider it a relatively small number."

The number of mares a stallion can handle, without prejudicing his fertility or health, also depends on the quality of his book. A smaller book with a high number of maiden and barren mares may well require more covers than a larger one with more fertile mares. Nevertheless, many breeders think there is an upper limit. At the height of Alydar's popularity, when Calumet was experiencing financial difficulties, J. T. Lundy bred over a hundred mares to the stallion in order to keep the farm afloat. Some breeders feel that may have contributed to his becoming a more fractious horse. Walmac International, Gainesway, and the Vinery also have reputations for giving their more popular stallions unusually large books.

"I don't know about that," Annette responded. "You need to ask them. I'm sure they'll tell you because none of this is a secret. Once the resulting foals are registered and locked in with the Jockey Club, it becomes a matter of public record and you have a pretty good idea how many mares a stallion has been bred to. Bloodstock Research Information Services can also tell you crop size by year. I think Calumet and Walmac both have bred a large number of mares to their stallions, if demand warranted it. But you have to have the demand before you can increase a book. There are many days when I have four or five mares that want a specific stallion. There are also many days when no mare wants a specific stallion. So there's no way for us to project in advance when a mare is gonna knock on the door wanting to be bred."

Once an outside breeder has decided to apply for a contract service to a Claiborne stallion like Forty Niner, what does the breeder do? "Usually they'll contact us by phone or mail in the fall or early part of the winter"—Annette gave an example—"and say, 'I've got old Blue Belle here, can we have a Forty Niner season for her?' And at that point Seth will either say yes or no or put them on a waiting list. He'll generally approve a mare based on her quality and whether she physically suits Forty Niner insofar as he physically knows the mare. That's something obviously he can only do with a real lot of definition with the mares that live here. But most of the people who have bred to Forty Niner are pretty deeply in the horse business. Thankfully, Forty Niner has been very much sought after and we've had to turn down many people. So we're breeding the best ones with the best people. It's a combination of the best people and the best horses and what will suit the horse best."

In fact, most of the stallion seasons that Claiborne controls are issued only to approved mares, and that's an important reason the farm annually averages 15 percent stakes winners. "If you call up and ask for a season to most of our stallions," Annette emphasized, "we're not going to automatically send you a contract with the mare's name blank. You have to tell us who it's gonna be and then she has to pass muster. If something befalls that approved mare and she can't be bred, you can't substitute another mare unless she's also approved."

The strict control that Seth Hancock exercises over which mares are sent to Forty Niner, of course, doesn't extend to every stallion on the farm. Most of the horses standing at Claiborne come from a different era, when almost every decent stallion prospect was syndicated for millions of dollars. Managing a syndicated stallion is considerably different from managing a homebred or privately owned stud because the individual shareholders generally have the right to breed to the mare of their choice. If a shareholder in Mr. Prospector, for example, wants to exercise or sell his season, neither he nor any potential buyer needs Seth Hancock's approval to breed to a particular mare. Of course, after paying $200,000 for a season, not many buyers are foolish enough to totally ignore Seth Hancock's experience and advice. And even then, Seth influences the quality of a syndicated stallion's book through the breeding rights the farm receives for standing the horse.

"We get four annual breeding rights for standing each syndicated horse that are referred to as ABRs," Annette elaborated. "We can do anything with those breeding rights that we want, including approving the mare. ABRs are noncumulative. We only get four a year. Just because we used three this year, that doesn't mean we get five next year. ABRs are the compensation a stud farm gets for standing the stallion. It's kind of a management fee and also covers costs like maintaining the night watchman, presenting the stallion to the mares, and so forth. In addition, an advertising and board bill is also charged for each stallion. Expenses run about $1,800 a year per share, which is billed quarterly to each shareholder. Most of our syndications are comprised of either thirty-six or forty shares with thirty-two share syndicates for a couple of the older stallions."

Claiborne has two basic options with its ABRs. It can breed one of its mares to the stallion or sell its seasons on the bloodstock seasons market. When a breeding right or season is sold, it is always sold at the farm's advertised price in order to protect the shareholders' investment. "With a homebred stallion like Forty Niner, of course," Annette contrasted, "there are no breeding rights because the farm owns the stallion and it would be like giving ABRs to itself. But for Easy Goer, which Mr. Ogden Phipps owns, we do receive four ABRs. Seth, if he so chooses, could sell a season or breed to Easy Goer off those breeding rights and not have to answer to anyone. Or he could sell the mare in foal to Easy Goer, the weanling, the yearling, or whatever off of those breeding rights. On some of these stallions there are also trainer's breeding rights, and we pretty much wait for them to tell us what they're going to do."

The purchase and sale of stallion seasons is itself a complex process and typically begins the previous summer. If Claiborne intends to sell a season, either for itself or for a client, it normally starts the process right after the close of the breeding season in early July. "There's usually an auction of stallion seasons at the same time as the Summer Select Sale," Annette explained. "Various bloodstock agents normally handle the sale of those seasons, which are usually *no-guarantee* seasons. And because they are no guarantee, the prices they will be bought for then will be less than later on because the buyer is gambling that the stallion will still be hale and hearty by the time the breeding season starts five to seven months later. So the older the stallion, the more risky it can be and usually the price is lower compared to what it would be closer to the breeding season. The closer it gets to breeding time, the more expensive no-guarantee seasons usually are because there's less risk. Also if someone buys a no-guarantee season to a freshman sire hoping his two-year-olds will run and six months later he hasn't had a starter, then obviously the value of that season can be less. But on an established horse, like a Mr.

Prospector or Danzig, what they paid last summer is probably going to be lower than what they have to pay now. Of course, the value of their seasons doesn't fluctuate that much because they're made horses. The greatest number of seasons are applied for in October and November, with November being the peak month."

It was half-past six and I could see that Annette was ready to go home. In parting, I asked her to talk about those clients with whom Claiborne has had a long-standing boarding relationship. Annette proceeded alphabetically. "Well, for major clients that have ten to twenty mares and for whom Claiborne is their home base, the list includes: Peter E. Blum and Christiana Stables which is owned by Mrs. Lunger and administered by Richard Jones. They board with us and other places as well. They were the owners of Go for Wand. Go for Wand was raised here but not foaled here. She came in at the side of her mother. Then there's Ed Cox, Jr., and Mrs. Martha Gerry who used to race under the name of Lazy F Ranch. She raced Forego, who was born and raised here. Howard B. Keck, who raced Ferdinand, boards exclusively with us. Then there's Henryk de Kwiatkowski, who owns Kennelot Stables. He lives primarily in the Bahamas but travels quite a bit. He raced Danzig and Conquistador Cielo, both of which are at stud here. Loblolly Stables, which is John Ed Anthony, is another important client. He retired Cox's Ridge to us and stood him privately for a year or two. Cox's Ridge is one of the few horses that has gone from a private stallion to a syndicated stallion. Mr. Anthony also brought in Vanlandingham and Demons Begone, who is privately maintained. The Phipps family is very important to us and includes Ogden Phipps, Ogden "Dinny" Mills Phipps, Cynthia Phipps, and Heidi Doubleday. They're all Phippses one way or another, board here, and are major shareholders in Easy Goer, Private Account, and Seeking the Gold. When Greentree was sold to Gainesway a couple of years ago, Mrs. John Hay Whitney moved her horses here and now breeds under her own name. If you want a more complete record of our clients, you should talk with Jim Freiss, our financial manager, because he bills them every month."

15

MONEY
MANAGEMENT

*A*cting on Annette Couvalt's suggestion, I made an appointment to meet with Jim Freiss in his office the following afternoon. As the chief financial officer at Claiborne and one of Seth Hancock's principal advisors, I figured he would have some interesting stories to share about the challenges involved in keeping the farm solvent. A trim, relaxed man in his early forties with a droll sense of humor, Freiss leaned back in his chair and confided that he comes from a family sharply attuned to the jingle of money. When I asked him how an accountant could get into the horse business, he laughed and responded, "It happened indirectly. I spent my summers during high school being a money runner at Churchill Downs. I would take a bag of money from one station to another and later in the day back to the big money room. The reason I did that was because my dad worked in one of the money rooms during Derby week. He normally worked as a bank accountant and would take his vacation and work at Churchill Downs."

Jim was further connected to horse racing during his youth because his parents rented an extra room in the house to a parimutuel clerk who worked at Churchill Downs when the meet moved there from neighboring Midwest tracks. "He always stayed with us," Jim recollected with an amused grin, "and on Sunday mornings when we would all get up and take a bus to downtown Louisville to have breakfast and go to church, he would have his *Racing Form* with him at *all* times. I kind of got a feel for it and developed a liking of it. He used to tout Derby horses and got me watching for it."

After high school Jim Freiss lost track of the horses for a while. He worked his way through college and put a hitch in with a CPA firm. Five years later he made a fateful call to a friend who was a partner in the firm that was doing Claiborne's accounting and told him he was looking to get out of public practice into something private. The friend advised Jim to talk to Claiborne because he was recommending that they hire an in-house CPA to improve their financial management. "I wasn't too excited about being in the horse business at that time," Jim confided, "because I was struggling just to make ends meet. I was married, had a child and bills to pay. But I said, 'I'll at least take the interview.' Then, when the partner brought me to the farm and we drove through the gate, I said, 'That's it. Where do I sign! If they want me, I'm ready.' And it's been heaven and real interesting ever since."

Whatever else Jim Freiss had learned in college and the business world, financially managing a horse farm wasn't one of the subjects. I asked him if he had to invent a way to deal with it. "Interesting you say that because Claiborne sets a trend in so many different areas. The second year I was here I went by and asked Seth if he would object if I put a computer in and computerized the operation. Well, after he picked himself up off the floor, he said, 'If you really think we should, you can at least look into it.' This was when horse farms and computers just didn't mix. People had everything in their head and did everything by hand."

The idea of relying on people's fleeting memory or trying to decipher shoe boxes full of illegible receipts sounded like an accounting nightmare. "Initially it was pretty challenging," Jim agreed. "But it wasn't like the attitude was, Don't bring a computer around here, we don't want modern technology. It was more, We want hands-on horsemanship."

Nevertheless, Seth Hancock gave Jim a chance because "Everything we do, we pretty much do the same for all the horses. We have to bill them for board and keep, charge veterinary expenses. Payroll is just like any other business. Stallions, you have so many shares per stallion and each one has a mare to be bred to it. It's got to be recorded when that mare was bred and what she had and who's to get money for it. All that has to be billed out, and it's a lot of work when you have twenty to twenty-five stallions and they all have thirty or forty shareholders."

Jim Freiss spent the better part of his first year trying to find a workable accounting system within the horse industry in Kentucky and couldn't. Then he heard about an accountant in California who was doing something very similar to hotel accounting on a horse farm there. After talking it over with Seth Hancock, Jim flew out to the coast to look at the system and meet the guy that developed it. Favorably impressed, he invited the accountant to come to Kentucky.

"I told him I would give him a thousand dollars when he got off the plane if he would stay a week," Jim recollected. "At the end of the week, if I liked what he did, I told him that we would sign a deal based on his estimates of what it would cost to set up. The guy came prepared. He did all the homework he said he would do and spent the week installing it. I liked it. It was a very flexible system, and we've actually made very few changes to it over the past fifteen years. It allowed us to bill with tremendous flexibility, which was important because each horse and each client is a story and you have to be able to handle all kinds of situations. Anyhow, we bought the system and now all the horse farms around here have one. After Seth hired me, they all started hiring financial managers too. So we set a trend."

One of the major advantages of Claiborne's new accounting system was that it allowed Freiss to estimate the farm's costs more rationally and determine what the charges should be for various services. Since the boarding of horses is a major expense, I asked Jim to talk about the day rates Claiborne charges. "For mares, foals, and yearlings, we currently charge $23 a day," he replied. "Then there's a veterinary charge of $50 a month and blacksmith charges of $10 for trimming and an additional $20, when necessary, for shoes. The three standard charges are board, vet, and blacksmith. So it costs about $750 a month or $9,000 a year to take care of a mare, a foal, or a yearling."

From an industry perspective, Claiborne's flat vet fee is a particularly good deal. For fifty bucks a month each mare gets vaccinated and wormed and is examined as many times as she needs to be during the breeding season with no additional charge. "We have enough horses," Jim explained, "that we can maintain a resident vet in Dr. Kaufman. Most farms have vets that just come to them certain days a week, and that's all done by specific charge."

The day rate for stallions is even more expensive because of the round-the-clock observation and greater handling they require during the breeding season. Claiborne charges $40 a day for stallions plus the vet and shoeing fee, which comes to $1,280 a month or some $15,360 a year. Added to that is a prorated charge for the stallion advertising that appears in such trade publications as *The Blood-Horse* and *Thoroughbred Times*, which typically runs $4,000 a month.

"So, with a forty-share syndicate"—Jim tallied up the charges— "the annual advertising cost for a stallion would be $48,000, plus $15,360 in maintenance fees for a total of $63,360. If you divide that figure by forty shares, you get an annual cost of $1,584 per share. So if a shareholder sells their season, say, to Majestic Light for the stud fee of $25,000, then, assuming they find a buyer, they will realize a net income from owning that share of $23,416 for that year."

Of course, the income a shareholder earns can vary dramatically depending on the syndication's terms. Some syndications (like Secretariat's) include drawings for additional shares if a horse is bred more times than the number of shares. "So if there's a forty-share syndicate and a horse is bred to sixty mares," Jim explained, "then there are twenty extra shares. What generally happens in that case is that every other year each shareholder will get two shares instead of one. You might not draw the extra share the first year, but if you don't then you'll get it the second one. The third year you put all the names back in a pile and draw again to see who gets the extra shares when. How many extra shares there are depends on how many extra mares the stallion can be bred to. If he can only breed to forty, then you don't get any extra bonuses. So the bonus depends on the fertility and popularity of the stallion."

The investment value of a share in a good stallion interested me. I knew that Seth Hancock had originally syndicated Secretariat in thirty-two shares for over $6 million. Since one share cost $190,000, what was the ballpark return on that share over Secretariat's entire career? "I can't be exact," Jim replied. "But I'd say, if you had one share all the way through, you'd be counting your profits in the millions."

So even though people thought $190,000 was a lot of money to pay for a share in Secretariat in 1973, it turned out to be a real bargain? "It sure did. His first foals that were sold as yearlings averaged $600,000 and then they went up. So you made millions of dollars if you kept a share and had a mare in foal to Secretariat every two out of four years and then sold the foal. Later you prayed for a filly because of Secretariat's reputation as a producer of outstanding fillies. Same thing happened with Nijinsky, Mr. Prospector—all the good stallions—you made a ton of money, if you were one of the original shareholders."

Of course, it can work the other way, even with a good stallion. When Halo was syndicated for $36 million, or $900,000 a share, in the inflated market of 1984, the shareholders didn't anticipate the dramatic plunge in stud fees and income that was coming. What looked like a good investment when Halo's stud fee was $125,000 was very much less attractive when the market had driven it down to $45,000. "That's why you don't begrudge a shareholder that earns several million dollars," Jim observed. "Because there's not many of them. If a man can get a $200,000 stud fee for his horse, that's what everybody is shooting for. That's what we're all trying to do, have that one horse that's gonna carry us, give us the glory, and put us in the winner's circle."

I asked Jim if he could place a cash value on the stud services that Claiborne annually manages. "That's hard to say. If you added up the stud fees of all our stallions, it comes close to a million dollars. If all of them were bred to forty mares, you'd get a figure of $40 million. But it gets trickier than that because some stallions breed to sixty mares and others that are real old (like Nijinsky II) to only thirty mares. So the value of a particular stallion depends on how many mares he can breed and then whether or not it's a live-foal contract and how many live foals ensue. Some stallions you sell on a no-guarantee basis, so it depends on how many you sold. And it would vary from year to year depending on how each horse was handled. So that $40 million figure doesn't mean anything. You can't do anything with it, you can't go to a bank with it, it doesn't belong to us. It doesn't even belong to ten guys but probably eight hundred people. So it's really not very negotiable."

Since most of Claiborne's income has been traditionally derived from the four annual breeding rights it gets for managing its syndicated stallions, I asked Jim to talk about how those rights are converted into cash. "It's also difficult to answer that simply," he replied, "because a lot of our best breeding rights are not converted to cash but used each year when we breed a stallion to one of our best mares. In those cases we get zero cash. Of course, we hope that those four mares will produce four foals and those four foals will either be sold as high-priced yearlings or be given to the racing manager, race well, and generate racing revenue. So our actual cash income varies from year to year. If we sell some of our rights on a live-foal basis, a $50,000 stud fee might be worth $200,000. If we sold it on a nonguarantee, it would usually be worth half of that. So it's hard to generalize anything in the industry as being worth this or that."

The breeding game has certainly changed since the 1980s when a stallion season to Northern Dancer reportedly went for over $1 million and Nijinsky went for $450,000. "Those were some boom years," Jim acknowledged. "If you sold your season you got a lot of money. If you bred your mare and then sold the resulting yearling you got even more money. Seattle Dancer went for $13.1 million in 1985."

In the 1990s, with stud fees plummeting, there is less incentive for breeders to sell their stallion seasons. Instead, many of them are breeding foals for the midrange commercial market or, like Claiborne, sending them to the racetrack. When a breeder decides to use its stallion season rather than sell it, he always runs the risk that the mare will turn up barren or the foal crooked. And even if the foal is sound, there is a two-year delay in receiving any income from its sale.

"If you bred in year one, then it takes nearly two and a half years before the Keeneland July Select Yearling Sale." Jim explained the brutal economics. "And then, if you don't sell the yearling and decide to race it, you've got to wait for another year or two. So you could be looking at a four- to five-year delay before you get any return. The general rule is you have a five-year turnaround in this industry. Especially if you're racing. So if we want to breed to Danzig, raise the offspring, and maybe try to win a Derby or have a nice filly that comes back and is a producer for us, we have a five-year waiting period for a return of capital."

When I had been in the foaling barn with Seth Hancock earlier in the week, he told me that the farm had sold five of its best yearlings the previous summer to help out on its cash flow. I asked Jim Freiss if there was any predictable pattern to the sales of Claiborne's yearlings. "No. It varies a lot. Some years we might try and sell ten yearlings, other years three. Two years ago we didn't sell any yearlings at the Keeneland July Sale, which is where we normally get our big cash from."

What about the Keeneland September Sale? "The September Sale," Jim replied, "is where we sell horses we don't consider to be major potential stakes winners. We sell horses in September that we don't want to run, even though we think there's value there. We'll just turn them into cash. But in July we're trying to generate big cash to help us get through the expenses of maintaining a racing stable and running the farm.

"Our main objective," Jim emphasized, "is to race everything because we want to have that Derby winner rather than sell him for $700,000 as a yearling. Because if he wins the Derby, he's worth $10 million as a stud. So we hope we can generate enough money from the sale of breeding seasons that we don't use, from winning purse money at the racetrack, and commissions as a consigner of some of our clients' horses, that we can have the luxury of racing if we want to. And then we sell what we think we need to sell to raise enough cash so we can race some more. Also, we found out that it's very difficult to buy a proven high-quality broodmare and make a profit. Because if she's thrown a real good racehorse, she's probably too expensive given her chances of doing it again. We've found we do a lot better if we raise and race our own broodmares and bring the good ones back as producers rather than to try and buy them. That's another reason why we're into racing in a heavy way."

Keeping a large racing stable going, however, is expensive, and Claiborne has to weed the less productive horses out. "We typically start off with about fifty horses," Jim explained, "and usually finish the year with around twenty-five. Some of the fillies can't run very well, but they have valuable broodmare potential so we retire them and bring them back here to begin a new career as a broodmare. Seth relies on our trainers to tell him which fillies aren't going to make it because they're slow, unsound, or temperamentally unsuited for racing. Based on what they tell him and the filly's pedigree, Seth decides whether to sell her or bring her back and try her as a broodmare. If we sell her, then we generate revenue off the racetrack. If we bring her back, we hope to generate revenue from selling her offspring or from racing them."

With colts that don't race well, Claiborne is more ruthless. "Generally we sell them." Jim Freiss pulled no punches. "Because it takes a major, major horse, like a Forty Niner, to come back here as a stallion. When we sell a colt we usually try to sell it privately when we think it's at its maximum value, before it reaches the claiming ranks. We'd rather find somebody else that may want to give it a few more shots before running it as a claimer. Running our horses through the claiming ranks is our last choice."

What about a Mr. Prospector or a Danzig colt with a mediocre racing record? Do other breeders still gamble and buy a well-bred Claiborne colt like that in the hopes of getting lucky at stud? "That used to be the reason why we got a lot of money for a mediocre racehorse." Jim reminisced about the speculative 1980s. "But that's not the case anymore. That's been like a shock treatment to us. We used to have residual values with our colts because if a horse was a Danzig, a Mr. Prospector, or a Nijinsky, he was worth a lot of money. But nowadays, Black Tie Affair, who was the Horse of the Year, is only standing for $15,000. So imagine what a horse that is by a major horse, but wasn't a major winner, is going to be worth as a stallion? Nothing. So your residual value for colts is about gone. The only price you're gonna get for him is what he's worth as a racehorse."

Which brought up the interesting case of Academy Award. I wondered why Seth Hancock decided to stand Academy Award even though he apparently had physical problems early on and a mediocre race record. In fact, the horse didn't win a race until he was four. Was

Seth's decision to stand Academy Award a case where he liked the stallion's bloodlines (by Secretariat, out of a Mr. Prospector mare) and decided to take a shot with his pedigree? "Right. He had the bloodlines and the races he got beat in he ran under adverse conditions and still ran well. He had one of the things horsemen look for, heart. So he had pedigree and heart and did win five races, including a 1¼-mile Grade II turf race. And Peter Blum, the owner, was willing to stand him privately at a reasonable price. So Seth just said, 'Let's cross our fingers and hope that he produces to his pedigree.' But the bottom line is that it's extremely tough out there on all the colts. Fillies with poor race records and good pedigrees, on the other hand, still have some residual value as broodmares."

Returning to Claiborne's racing operation, Freiss told me it costs the farm about $25,000 a year to keep a horse in training. Included in that figure are such things as the trainer's day rates, vet charges, shoeing, vitamins, and vanning bills. Day rates average about $55, while vanning bills vary. When a horse is individually shipped from New York to Florida or Kentucky, the vanning bill can run as high as $700. But more often the bill is less because the vanning companies ship six or seven horses from various owners together, which cuts the cost for everyone to $200 or $300 a trip.

"If we fly a horse," Jim explained, "it could cost a couple of thousand. We do that if it's a stakes and we're trying to arrive shortly before the race. Some trainers like to run a horse right after it ships. Other trainers like to wait two weeks for it to acclimate itself. So it depends on the trainer and the race whether we fly or not."

How important, in the total scheme of things, is racing income to the farm? "It's real important," Jim reflected, "but it's also unreliable. We hope to break even. That's a good year. It's been our history that in every four- or five-year period, we have a major horse that wins a lot of money for us—like a Swale or a Forty Niner. So that's one *big* horse out of every 200 to 250 that we send to the track. If you have one good horse, it can carry you for a couple of years. Forty Niner won $2.7 million and that carries your racing stable for quite some time. On a year-to-year basis, we hope to break even, and Seth does an excellent job of managing the stable. You can't keep horses that are not producing for you. Yet you gotta know when to sell them. That's a real skill

Seth has. Still, it's not uncommon, in any given year, for us to lose money in the racing stable. On the bright side, every four to five years we do seem to come up with a major winner to balance things out."

The roller-coaster nature of racing income, even for a farm like Claiborne, is best illustrated by the purse money its horses won between 1988 and 1991. "In 1988 our net purses were $2 million," Jim reported. "But in 1989 they were $700,000. In 1990 they were $600,000. In 1991 about $800,000. So we average about $700,000 in our low years, but that gets raised by our good years."

Adding up the purse totals and dividing by four, Claiborne averaged about a million a year in racing income between 1988 and 1991. Since it had fifty horses in training at an annual cost of $25,000 apiece, the figures seemed to indicate that the farm just about broke even during those years. "Not really," Jim countered, "because we don't keep all fifty horses in training all year long. Like I said, Seth sells some privately, others we bring back here. So there is no magic formula. This is a very difficult business to try and budget."

Apparently so. I was beginning to appreciate that it takes not only a flexible accounting system but also a flexible accounting *mind* to work in the horse business. Still, there has to be a bottom line. Of all the sources of income, which ones really keep the farm in business? "Most of the time we rely on stud fees and horse sales," Jim responded. "The Hancocks have been doing this for close to a hundred years, so we pretty much know what our stud fees are going to be from year to year, unless we bring in a major horse or lose one. Then we take a look at last year in terms of what we did at the racetrack and, if Seth determines that this year's racetrack is not gonna be much different, then we know what that number is. And our expenses are gonna be pretty much the same. So we make up any difference between income and expenses by selling whatever number of yearlings we need to sell."

Even though the budgeting process is fraught with uncertainty, Jim Freiss does put together an annual financial plan that tries to anticipate operating expenses. "But the budgets are mostly on a broader scale," he reflected, "because so many specific items can be way off. For example, you hope you come up with that major racehorse before that sale so you can take your yearlings out of the sale. But if you don't come up with one, then you've got the sales to cover you. Of course, if you win a big race after the sales, you say, 'Well, darn, I wish we hadn't sold that yearling.' But once you've set a plan, you generally try to stick to it. If you planned as you went, you'd probably run into big trouble because today might be the day that one of your major horses dies. So if you'd planned on that racing income, you'd be up the creek. On the other hand, if you plan on not having any racing income and put everything in the sale, then you might have a horse that has a black-type work and suddenly instead of being worth $30,000, he's maybe a stakes horse and worth $300,000. So it's hard to plan on an individual basis."

Claiborne, of course, also generates income from several other sources. The burley tobacco crop, for example, brings in between $150,000 to $200,000 a year. "That's a nice, relatively predictable little plug for us." Jim couldn't resist the pun. "And it's also a positive tenant type of arrangement. All the tobacco proceeds don't go to the farm. Twenty-five percent of it goes to Claiborne employees who raise it on the side. Then we graze some cattle and that generates between $50,000 to $100,000 without costing us a lot, and there are some benefits for the land. We also sell horses for some of our clients and generate commission income. You can't budget it, but if you sell ten July Sale horses and they average $500,000, then you have a $5 million consignment. And if you get a 5 percent commission, you've just generated $250,000 through your expertise in raising good horses, prepping and selling them. At Keeneland the sales company makes 5 percent and the consigner makes 5 percent. So owners typically part with 10 percent as the cost of selling their horse."

Claiborne's largest source of income is its board operation, which brings in between $4 million and $5 million each year. Unfortunately, it isn't directly profitable. "We don't really make any money on the boarding fees." Jim reiterated what Seth Hancock had told me. "But it helps maintain the property, and hopefully you have some good clients and you can sell some horses for them and generate some commission income. You also hope they have some good horses like Private Account and Easy Goer that will come back and be a good stallion for you. Plus you gotta have a place for your own horses. So it all kind of makes good sense to have a boarding operation. You try to run it in a fashion where you don't lose a lot of money."

Why can't Claiborne make any money running its boarding operation? "Because there are so many things you can't charge through to the client," Jim replied. "Like a half-mile road that needs blacktopping every ninth year. Well, you can't turn around and charge that to the client. Same thing with fencing, which has a fifteen-year useful life. It gets worn and you have a mile's worth of fencing at six dollars a foot that costs $30,000. You can't pass that through. And every year there's some additional expense we have to absorb. So if you talk to a hundred farms, probably ninety of them will tell you they don't make any money boarding horses, but they try to make money through sales or replenishment of the stallion ranks from their clients."

I was beginning to see why even some very good horse farms, like Calumet and Spendthrift, have gone under. There's not a lot of margin for error. "It's a constant out-of-pocket business." Jim shook his head. "It's not a typical business. You can't go to the bank and finance and build a plant and then start building widgets and sell them to a market that you know wants them. With a horse farm, any day a storm might come through and knock down $100,000 worth of trees. Well, do you put them back or not? If you have eighteen barns and they all need painting, that's $3,000 each to paint them. It's tough to come up with $54,000 just to paint your barns. The bank's not gonna lend you the money hoping you sell that yearling for a million dollars or win a stakes race. It's a very tough business and you see a lot of farms going under right now. Where it's at right now is at the racetrack. Instead of selling their horses, people are increasingly gonna keep them and try to get some of those purses."

Ironically, the decline in the stallion and yearling markets is probably good for racing. One of the things that has hurt the sport the most in recent years has been that all the best horses were retired just as the general public began to take a fancy to them. The only really good horses that were kept on the track were the geldings like John Henry, Great Communicator, and Best Pal, which had no residual stud value. "The decline in stallion values has helped to keep more good horses running," Jim agreed. "The Breeders' Cup has also contributed because now, if you have a major horse, instead of retiring him as a three-year-old, you have an even better chance of winning that $3 million race as a four-year-old."

Beyond normal expenses, horse farms have needed to generate more racing income because of the rising costs of such things as pensions and medical benefits. "Medical expenses are skyrocketing and again we can't pass that through. Owners at boarding farms are a lot like owners at racetracks. They're willing to pay $55 a day, but not $60 or $65. So when the medical premiums go up we have to eat a lot of that, because we can't have our people working without medical coverage."

Similarly, rising horse insurance rates have taken their toll. "A lot of owners believe in insuring their horses," Jim emphasized. "And that expense, which runs around 5 percent, is just one more expense that owners have to add to day rates, vet fees, vanning, and the 10 percent cut given to both the trainer and jockey. So there isn't any extra fat. We insure our horses both on the farm and at the track. So if we think a horse is worth $500,000, then it costs us $25,000 a year on top of everything else. People don't talk about insurance but, if a horse is worth a lot to you and hasn't yet won any money, it's a considerable expense. And the bottom line is that we are in a luxury business and people will bail out if we keep raising our prices. So we operate under severe financial restraints. That's why you see a lot of farms going under."

Nevertheless, because of good horsemanship and shrewd management, Claiborne has continued to prevail. "Seth has done an outstanding job." Jim Freiss credited his boss. "Look at the position he was in when Mr. Hancock died in 1972. Claiborne was at the top then and everyone was taking potshots and trying to get a piece of it. That didn't happen. If you look at our stallion roster now, you'll see top horses and all of those, except Nijinsky, Seth brought in."

16

LORD OF
THE MANOR

*T*oward the end of my week's stay at Claiborne, on a warm, almost balmy afternoon, I pulled up a chair next to Seth Hancock's desk in the same office where both his father and grandfather had conducted their horse business. Apart from a brief encounter in the breeding shed, when Arazi's dam Danseur Fabuleux was being bred to Mr. Prospector, and in the foaling barn with the maiden mare San, we hadn't talked much since I had arrived. By mutual accord, I think, both of us had concluded that I should first get a feel for the farm. So my sense of the man, who was wearing simple work clothes, a nylon parka, and a baseball hat when I sat down, was framed more by what I had read and what his men had had to say about him than anything else.

As background, of course, I knew that the mantle of responsibility for running Claiborne had fallen upon Seth Hancock's shoulders early when his father, Bull Hancock, died suddenly from cancer in September of 1972. And that four months later, at the age of twenty-three, he got on the phone and syndicated Secretariat for a then-record $6 million. True, Seth had the counsel of such knowledgeable trustees as William Haggin Perry and Ogden Phipps to initially guide him, but the weight of following in the footsteps of a legendary father and superseding his older brother, Arthur, had to etch a certain gravity in his mind. To this day, when you meet Seth Hancock, the first impression you get is of a thoughtful and serious man.

At forty-three, of course, Seth Hancock has had twenty years to establish his own impressive track record. And the fact that Claiborne is still on top is a testament to his acumen. He's the man who presided over the successful transformation of the Claiborne stud from the reign of Nasrullah and Bold Ruler to the Raise a Native/Mr. Prospector and Northern Dancer/Danzig lines. Along the way he also bred such outstanding horses as Nureyev, Caerleon, Swale, and Forty Niner and recommended to breeder Ben Castleman the mating that produced Seattle Slew.

When it comes to business, Seth Hancock is obviously no slouch either. During the highly speculative 1980s, when many breeders mortgaged their futures in an attempt to cash in on the Arab and Japanese money that was feeding the ever-rising bloodstock market, Seth kept a steady hand. Because he didn't go into debt and overexpand, Claiborne weathered the collapse of the bloodstock market while such notable competitors as Calumet and Spendthrift went under.

Curious why his brother Arthur had left Claiborne to start Stone Farm so soon after Bull Hancock died, I opened by asking Seth if there was anything he wanted to say about the situation then. "Not really," he responded. "We just had some guidelines we had to live by. We had an advisory board that we had to report to, and Arthur felt constrained by it and wanted to strike out on his own."

So people's assumption that it was a horrible dynastic situation, fueled with bad blood, wasn't really true? "No. Arthur felt encumbered by the guidelines he had to operate under. He wanted to try and do his own thing, and obviously he's done a helluva job at it. He's made a great mark for himself, and it's worked out well for both parties."

Shifting our conversation back to horses, I asked Seth how he selects his stallions, especially how Danzig and Mr. Prospector came to Claiborne. "Well, Danzig was owned by Henryk de Kwiatkowski and raced by him," Seth recollected. "He wanted to breed a lot of his mares to Danzig. So it was a natural that Danzig came here where they were. We didn't know how good a racehorse Danzig was because he only raced three times. But with him being a son of Northern Dancer and Henryk committed to supporting him with his mares, that gave Danzig two very good legs up on making a successful sire. Plus Henryk let me set the stud fee at a price where we thought we could attract some good outside mares. His fee started out at $20,000."

Was the modest initial stud fee because Danzig had only raced three times and outside people didn't yet have confidence in him? "That's right. We were going to breed Danzig to fifty mares the first year, six to ten of which would have been Mr. de Kwiatkowski's. So we had to come up with forty to forty-five good outside mares to breed to the horse so he had a chance. It doesn't make any difference how good a stallion is, if he doesn't get good mares he's not going to make a good sire."

What about a stallion like Mr. Prospector, who started in Florida and then came to Claiborne? "Well, like I said earlier, Mr. Prospector was a made horse when he came here," Seth reiterated. "I had nothing to do with the success of Mr. Prospector. He was an outstanding sire before he came here and we were able to get good mares to him. But, hell, if he had stood anywhere he was going to get good mares off of what he had done in Florida."

And how good was Mr. Prospector's original book of mares in Florida? "Fair. There's only so good a book a horse can get in Florida, but he did very well with the book he had."

I wondered if a stallion had ever gotten a mediocre book in a state like Florida and done well, but then done worse with a better book of mares in Kentucky. Was that a concern of Seth's with Mr. Prospector? "It has happened before and I was worried about it," Seth acknowledged. "I said something to Peter Brant who owns several shares in the horse and he said, 'I understand what you're talking about, but if you look at the good horses that Mr. Prospector has sired, they've been out of pretty damn good mares.' And he was right. Like Miswaki was out of a good Buckpasser mare, and several of his other good horses were out of the same type of good mares he was going to be getting when he got here. So Peter allayed my fears."

So what makes for a good broodmare? What does Seth look for when approving a mare for his stallions? "Basically you look for the same thing in each. In a stallion you look for race record, pedigree, and conformation, in that order. And that's basically what you look for in a broodmare. I think in a broodmare, pedigree is really important. If you have a stallion and he has no race record, you're in trouble with him because without it people aren't going to breed to him. But if you have a mare and she has no race record, I still give her a chance if she's got a real good family."

What about the mare who has a poor race record but comes from a good family? "If she ran ten or twelve times and didn't hit the board," Seth replied, "I wouldn't want her no matter how well she was bred."

Trainers constantly emphasize conformation when they look at a horse. How important is it in selecting a stallion? "Well, you've spent time around the breeding shed while you've been here. You've looked at each one of those horses and seen they're all made differently. Some of them have beautiful hind legs and some don't. Some of them are a little over at the knee, and Majestic Light is pretty crooked. You look at Easy Goer and he's a little bit of a funny-made horse in front. So I don't really think that conformation is supremely important in picking stallions. If he has enough race record to attract attention and enough of a pedigree so that he actually has a chance to make it, even if he has a few conformation flaws, I think you can breed away from those with the type of mares you send him."

In recent years the texture of Claiborne's stallion roster has narrowed considerably. The current roster is dominated by Raise a Native blood through such stallions as Mr. Prospector, Conquistador Cielo, Majestic Light, Easy Goer, Forty Niner, and Seeking the Gold; and with Northern Dancer blood as passed on by Danzig, Nijinsky, Topsider, and Ferdinand. In addition, Damascus is represented by Private Account and Ogygian and In Reality by Believe It and Proper Reality. Gone, however, is the Domino blood of Double Jay and Ack Ack, the Princequillo blood of Round Table, and the Hyperion blood of Forli.

Perhaps more important, there is very little Nasrullah blood at

Claiborne now and none from Ribot. Since Ribot is a major influence for stamina in the breed and his son Tom Rolfe and grandson Hoist the Flag stood at Claiborne, I asked Seth if he missed the Ribot influence in his stud.

"We'd love to have it," Seth replied. "But the sons of Hoist the Flag haven't really bred on, and we've just bought two shares in Pleasant Colony to put some stamina in our broodmares and hopefully come up with a good stallion prospect."

What about the Buckpasser line, the other major contemporary source of stamina? "We're not worried about that," Seth replied. "His importance to the breed is gonna be through his females. But I don't feel the Ribot line on the top is gonna die out. Unfortunately, we don't have any of it right now, so we're going to other places to look for it. We don't really have any Nasrullah now either. We put a lot of eggs in Spectacular Bid's basket and he didn't come through. That's why we were very anxious to stand Capote and weren't able to get that done. But there'll be other good sons of Seattle Slew, and maybe we'll come up with one of them."

As a way of possibly getting a future Nasrullah-line stallion, is Claiborne breeding some of its mares to Seattle Slew? "We are breeding to Seattle Slew and Slew o' Gold. Of course, if we hadn't had bad luck with Swale, we would have had the most attractive son of Seattle Slew standing here. But that wasn't meant to be."

Historically, there have been several cycles in the development of Claiborne's stud where first stamina and then speed-oriented stallions have been desirable. In the 1920s and 1930s, Seth's grandfather brought over Sir Gallahad III and Blenheim II as a stamina outcross to breed to American mares that had a lot of Domino speed in them. Then, a generation later, his father brought in Nasrullah to breed speed into the stamina-laden mares that were daughters of Sir Gallahad and Blenheim. In the 1990s, with the proliferation of the speedy daughters and granddaughters from the Raise a Native, Northern Dancer, and Bold Ruler lines, does Seth Hancock think the time is soon coming when the breed will need stamina-oriented stallions again?

"I sure do," he agreed. "But I don't know where to go get it. When I first took over the farm, we had Le Fabuleux here. He was going to be a great source of stamina. As far as I was concerned, he was a bad failure. Pronto was going to be a source of stamina and a complete outcross. He was a terrible stallion. So the luck I've had with those type of horses hasn't been real good. I was thinking about Festin. I liked Festin, but I talked to a few breeders and asked, 'What about this horse, would you want to breed to him?' They said, 'No.' When I asked why, they said, 'Well, he comes from too far out of it and has no speed.' Well, hell, I'm not gonna sit here and breed forty mares to the horse myself to try to prove other people wrong. So I gave up on the idea of standing Festin."

Interesting. Seth Hancock was telling me that, as a breeder, he wants more stamina in his stud, but as a stallion manager he can't afford to sacrifice speed to get it. Okay, then, what about getting speed from the mares? That's the way the breed first started when those quick-twitch, aerobically oriented British Hobby mares were bred to distance-running Oriental stallions that had, in biological terms, been genetically selected for their anaerobic ability to process more efficiently the lactic acid that governs fatigue. Or is it the case that contemporary breeders and bloodstock agents no longer have confidence that the mares can pass on the speed and think it always has to come from the stallion?

"Yeah, I think so," Seth replied. "But you know, we can't even prove stamina in our mares anymore because we don't have any long races to prove it in. I mean, the Coaching Club American Oaks is what, a mile and a quarter, and it's the longest race there is for fillies. The Breeders' Cup Distaff used to be a mile and a quarter and now it's a mile and an eighth. We really have no proving grounds for stamina in the broodmares, so we feel like we have to come with stamina from the sires. The Belmont winners should be the greatest sources of stamina that there is. But the Belmont winners, as a group, have really made inferior sires. I mean Stage Door Johnny, Riva Ridge, Little Current, Summing . . . that's not a very impressive list."

What about Conquistador Cielo? "He won the Belmont and has been a pretty good sire. But he really wasn't a stamina horse. I mean, anybody knows if you run a mile in 1:33 in the Metropolitan you're a speed horse. He stole the Belmont. He caught a sloppy track, it just was his day. Plus he probably beat a pretty inferior group of horses. I think Gato del Sol was second and Linkage was third, and both of them have gone on to be bad stallions, so they probably weren't very good racehorses either."

In any event, Seth Hancock agrees that finding new stallions with both stamina and a fast enough turn of foot to win in America isn't going to be easy. Going to Europe for them probably isn't going to work either because most of their successful stallions are sons of American sires that trace to the Phalaris blood of Northern Dancer, Raise a Native, and Nasrullah. With the possible exception of the Dark Ronald line in Germany, does that then leave South America, South Africa, New Zealand, and Australia as the most likely future sources for both stamina and outcrosses?

"You're probably right," Seth reflected. "But then I don't know if you would really know what you were getting."

Which brought us back to the question of a horse like Festin. What if Festin does become successful? "Then he'll be the most desirable stud in America. Just because he's a complete outcross and because he's going to be a great source of stamina. But if he passes on his own running style, he's not going to get any good two-year-olds. So then the danger is that everyone that is breeding to him is going to quit and he'll be dead in the water before he even gets started."

Given the fact that a lot of Thoroughbred owners have deep pockets, why is there such an emphasis on two-year-olds? Why don't more breeders take their time and breed horses for winning at three, four, and five?

"Well, take a sire like Devil's Bag," Seth responded. "He's pretty much proven that you can afford to wait on his horses because he's come up with some good older horses like Twilight Agenda and like that filly, Devil's Orchid, that Mandella trains. We bought two shares in Pleasant Colony and if any of those ever win a two-year-old race, I'd be surprised. But you *know* it's worth waiting on them. But the stallions you *don't* know are worth waiting on, you feel like a fool waiting on a four-year-old maiden by a sire and then the sire turns out to be a bust at everything and you've pissed away two years' worth of training expenses on something that wasn't worth waiting on to begin with."

Given that some of Claiborne's best stallions—Nijinsky, Mr. Prospector, and Cox's Ridge—were getting old, I wondered how Seth

Hancock would try to replace them. Looking at his roster, I could see that Seth has a number of their sons on line hoping they'll be effective replacements. For Nijinsky, there's Ferdinand; for Mr. Prospector, Forty Niner and Seeking the Gold; for Cox's Ridge, Vanlandingham.

"Well, nobody will replace Nijinsky," Seth asserted. "But we hope that Ferdinand will be a good sire. He's not an outcross, but he certainly ought to get distance horses. I'd be shocked if he got a bunch of good two-year-olds. Then we have Ogygian, a son of Damascus, who will have three-year-olds running. We've got Forty Niner and Ferdinand that will have two-year-olds this year. We have Seeking the Gold, Easy Goer, and Proper Reality that have yearlings this year. So we're just hopeful that those young horses will come along and do well. We've been in this situation before when Damascus and Sir Ivor started getting old. We're always bringing in new horses and hoping that they'll hit."

What about stallions like Honest Pleasure, Spectacular Bid, and Track Barron that didn't make it at Claiborne and had to be relocated? What criteria does Seth use to decide it's time to let a stallion go? "We try to evaluate our stallions on the basis of their first three crops, take a reading and see if they're doing what we want them to do. If a high-priced horse is doing okay, he still may be moved compared to a low-priced horse that's doing okay and is overachieving compared to his opportunities. The lower-priced horse might stay. So a lot depends on how they do compared with our expectations."

How important are the statistical earnings indexes that are published in *The Blood-Horse* and *Thoroughbred Times* in influencing Seth's decision about the fate of a stallion? "They're important," he acknowledged, "but I don't pay any attention to them because I feel like I know what the horses are doing at the track and numbers sometimes lie. So I just try and take an overall view of it without looking at any particular numbers."

A quick glance at Claiborne's stallion roster makes it clear that Seth Hancock is partial to sons and grandsons of Raise a Native. He stands six of them, including Majestic Light by Majestic Prince; Easy Goer and Talinum by Alydar; and Conquistador Cielo, Forty Niner, and Seeking the Gold by Mr. Prospector. Why does he stand so many Raise a Native–line stallions?

"I don't think you can have too much of a good thing," Seth responded. "And I think sons of Mr. Prospector are the best things going right now. With Forty Niner I knew Claiborne was gonna support him and that we could afford to stand him for a price where we could attract real good mares to him. I knew that the Phipps family was going to support Seeking the Gold. So I didn't worry about bringing in either one of those two horses, even though we had a lot of that blood, because I knew where a great big bulk of their support was gonna come from. If some guy now had a real good son of Mr. Prospector and I went to talk to him and said, 'We'd really like to stand this horse at Claiborne Farm,' and he said, 'Fine. You can buy him outright, here he is,' I would ask him, 'You don't want to stand for a quarter of him and support him?' And if he said, 'Naw, I'm not in the breeding game, that doesn't interest me,' well, I'd back away. Because if this guy's not going to support him, I'm not gonna put my neck in a noose for him. If he doesn't have enough confidence in the horse to support him, then it's going to shake me a little bit as to what I think about him."

One horse that Seth Hancock clearly had high hopes and affection for was his homebred Forty Niner, who many industry pundits were predicting would become the leading freshman sire. What kind of feedback was Seth getting to the initial crop of two-year-olds in training that Forty Niner had? Did any of them have the look of being big runners?

"Absolutely." Seth's face lit up. "I just came back from Aiken, South Carolina, and we have some good horses coming. Tourney is the best one that I think is out there. He's out of Birth, a Believe It mare. Her first foal was a horse called Rail that was stakes-placed as a two-year-old last year. Henryk de Kwiatkowski's got a filly out of Sabine that looks very promising. We have Tour, a filly in California with Richard Mandella, that looks like a runner, and a colt with Paco Gonzalez out of Low End that he likes. Greentree has a colt, Apprentice, out of Young Ballerina that looks good and Jim Taefel's got Klondiker out of Graceful Darby that he likes. We have one out of No Choice called Tackle we like and another out of Level called Miter that's highly thought of so far. There's one out of Contredance, and Scotty Schulhofer has one Tactical Advantage out of a mare called Twitchet that he likes. So there's a bunch of good prospects out there."

Comparing first crops, I wondered if Seth Hancock can tell when a young sire is going to make it. Does he get a feeling from seeing the foals on the farm that is later borne out at the track? "Well, you like to think you know what you're doing," Seth reflected. "By and large, you like the offspring of your stallion. You can't afford not to. But we liked the Polish Navys a lot early on and so far they've been disappointing. There have also been cases when we didn't like the offspring of a stallion. We didn't like Secretariat's first crop and we were worried about him right from the get-go. None of them looked like him. Some were gray, some were bay, some were big and some light-boned. He wasn't stamping his get. That can be all right as long as they look like athletes. But the first bunch of Secretariat's just didn't look the part. His second crop was a helluva lot better and performed a lot better, and at the end of the day Secretariat was a damn good sire."

Within the industry Secretariat is considered a good "filly sire" but a failure as a sire of sires. I wondered if, looking at his pedigree—with such strong broodmare sire influences as Princequillo and Discovery—it was predictable that Secretariat would be more successful as a filly sire. "No, not really," Seth disagreed. "Sons of Bold Ruler were very successful stallions and Secretariat was too. It just happens that he got better fillies. But you couldn't know that in advance from looking at his pedigree. After the fact, I guess you can say his strength as a sire came more from Princequillo and the female side of his pedigree."

If Risen Star takes after his daddy Secretariat, he may be more successful as a broodmare sire too. What does Seth think about him as a stallion prospect? "I really wouldn't be too crazy about him," he responded. "He was a damn good racehorse, but he's a big horse and getting big, unathletic-looking foals. But I'm sure that's what they were saying when Pleasant Colony went to stud, and he's made a damn good sire. I don't think Risen Star will be a sensation right off the bat, but that's not to say that down the road he won't be a good solid sire because he is out of a pretty good mare and he's by Secretariat. So I'd give him a chance."

Of course, a good stallion is only part of the equation. To be successful, good mares also have to be approved for him. How does Seth decide which mares to approve for a specific stallion? "We get applications to the studs every day." He explained the process. "I just took two of them to our booker, Annette Couvalt, a few minutes ago. One of them was a mare they wanted to breed to Forty Niner. Not a bad race mare. Decent enough as far as the racing part, but she's by Secreto and he doesn't really do too much for me. And the female family was okay, but nothing great. His book is full, so it would take a better-than-average mare to get to Forty Niner at this stage of the game. So I passed on her. The other application was a nice mare, but it was for Nijinsky and he's old and we're not breeding any outside mares to him."

While Seth can easily punch up the family history and race record of the mares that outside breeders submit for his approval, he often doesn't know that much about their conformation. "If I'm on the fence about whether to accept the mare or not I'll call the guy and ask, 'What kind of mare is this? Is she a big mare, small mare? Got any conformation flaws?' If it's somebody I know and he okays her, then that's fine with me. If it's somebody I don't know, they're gonna have to really be strong in every category to make it to one of these horses that's really popular."

In deciding on a specific mating, how important are dosage, inbreeding, and nicks to Seth as breeding tools? "Dosage I don't even think about," Seth categorically stated. "If I bred 40 percent stakes winners, and all of them were horses that never won beyond seven-eighths of a mile, I'd be tickled to death. Maybe I did breed a bunch of short horses, but those son of a guns could run and that's the name of the game. With inbreeding when I do our matings, as long as they're not inbred closer than the third generation, I don't worry about it. But I don't set out to inbreed either. Nicking? Yes, that's important. If we've got a mare here from one female family and it's produced well with Nijinsky, that mare's going back to Nijinsky as long as everything else is okay in my mind."

What about breeding Raise a Native–line stallions to Buckpasser mares? "That's a good nick and that's probably how Seeking the Gold was bred for the Phipps family—because Miswaki was one of the first good Mr. Prospectors and he's out of a Buckpasser mare. So we said, 'What the hell, it worked well once, let's try it again.' And there comes Seeking the Gold. Same thing with Easy Goer. So now if a breeder comes to me with a Buckpasser mare and says, 'What do you think?' I'd say, 'Well, Buckpasser's worked well with two lines we got here—the Northern Dancer and the Raise a Native lines. So let's talk about the mare. Is she a big mare or a small mare? Does she have a lot of speed? Does she want to run a route of ground? What kind of temperament does she have?' I think with Seeking the Gold, he's gonna have to be bred to mares that are pretty levelheaded, because he's a little on the hyper side and was as a racehorse. So if I was picking a mare for him, I'd try to breed to a mare that had a good temperament."

Seth's brother Arthur had also stressed the importance of temperament, particularly when breeding to Ribot-line horses. "That Ribot sure was a high-tempered bastard." Arthur graphically related an incident when he was still at Claiborne. "We had one of Ribot's daughters on the farm and one day Daddy's bulldog walked behind her when we were putting up the yearlings. And she kicked him in the head and knocked him to the other side of the building. I don't know why it didn't kill him. He shook his head and wasn't quite right for a few days after that. But my point is that you would want to breed anything by Ribot to something with good temperament."

Halo and his sons are also "hot headed" stallions, in Arthur's view. "Halo has a lot of temperament. He'll run a bird out of his field, he's so territorial. I mean, a cat, some stray tom, went through there one day and Halo went through that field and that cat looked up and took off. And Halo chased right after him. It was the damnedest race you ever saw with the cat cutting one way then another and Halo right after him. We have Halo's son, Lively One, here now. And I went out in the field one day and he acted pretty territorial too. He reared up and I had to take my belt off to let him know to leave me alone. Sunday Silence was that way. He pawed Charlie Whittingham in the head and bit his groom. So just on temperament, you would never want to breed a Ribot mare to Halo. You might get a rogue, something that was mean. They both have mean streaks. Then again, it's such an inexact science you might breed that and turn out with a champion. Who knows? I think it depends on the nick. I put a lot of stock in nicks and what's worked."

Back with Seth in his office, he elaborated on other nicks that have worked for him. "With Nijinsky the absolute dynamite nick has been with Round Table–line mares. Anything from Prince John and Prince-quillo. Pleasant Colony/Stage Door Johnny is an awesome nick right now. Northern Dancer/Buckpasser's been great. Private Account on top of the Tom Rolfe line has worked. On the other hand, the Bold Ruler line has been terrible with Nijinsky. I'd never do anything like that again."

Does it matter much who's on top and who's on the bottom in a nick? "Yes, it does a lot. You should get Jack Werk's comments. He puts out *Owner/Breeder*. He talked about this at a conference we had in Lexington last fall and it was very interesting. We thought that the Northern Dancer/Buckpasser cross was a real good cross. So we figured that Nijinsky/Buckpasser would be a good cross. We were wrong. It's been a bad cross. It's hard to figure out why, but it has been. If you put Round Table on top of Nijinsky mares, I'm not sure it would work. I wouldn't be afraid to try it, but just because it works well one way doesn't mean the reverse would work."

What about Claiborne's Damascus-line horses, Private Account and Ogygian? Any good nicks there? "With Private Account, Hoist the Flag and Ribot have been the absolute best. With Ogygian we can't say yet. But those are two different kinds of horses. Private Account gets more of a rangy type of foal whereas Ogygian gets a blocky, speed-looking horse pretty much like himself. Ogygian is more likely to get precocious two-year-olds than horses that will win a 1¼-mile race."

Of all the stallions at Claiborne, Devil's Bag perhaps best illustrates that a stallion's race record is sometimes less a harbinger of his performance at stud than his pedigree. "Devil's Bag was a great two-year-old," Seth reflected. "Maybe one of the greatest we've ever seen. We automatically figured he'd come out with a bunch of dynamite two-year-olds. When he didn't everybody was really disappointed, including myself. So you kind of take a step back and keep fooling around with them and then all of a sudden as they get older they get good. Why? Well, we were stupid to think he'd ever get two-year-olds because he's by Halo out of a Herbager mare and both of those lines are lines that are going to get better, older horses. So even though Devil's Bag was a brilliant horse, his genes and pedigree said he's gonna get horses that get better as they get older. And that's what's happened with horses like Twilight Agenda and Devil's Orchid."

Since Halo traces back to Turn-to, who was a real speedster, does that mean Halo picked up his stamina from the female side? "Maybe," Seth mused, "but if you look at his immediate parents, his daddy, Hail to Reason, sired a Belmont winner, so there's every right for Halo to get his stamina from him, too."

Hail to Reason's sire Turn-to also sired Sir Gaylord (sire of Habitat and Sir Ivor), Cyane (sire of Smarten), and Best Turn (sire of Cox's Ridge). Despite the obvious ability of the Turn-to line to generate runners, a lot of horsemen have been reluctant to embrace them because of their alleged mousy appearance and soundness problems. I wondered if Seth agreed with this prejudice. "Not really," he stated. "The Cox's Ridges have always sold well. But people are right, the Hail to Reason branch of it doesn't sell well, the Halos and all that. As far as soundness, certain strains of the Turn-to line were unsound. The Sir Gaylord/Drone side of it was unsound, but the Hail to Reason side with Halo and Roberto has been pretty sound."

Some stallions, like Halo, are cribbers, which means they're fond of grabbing wooden fences and stall doors with their teeth, arching their necks, and sucking air into their bellies. Some breeders think this makes a horse more vulnerable to colic. European breeders generally abhor not only cribbers, but also parrot-mouthed horses. I asked Seth what he thought of these prejudices. "I don't know." He shrugged his shoulders. "But they always have been prejudiced. I don't understand it. They turned Halo back because he was a cribber. He was bought as a stud horse by someone over there and they voided the sale when they found out he was a cribber. It's a stupid prejudice, I think. But that's their business, not mine."

Believe It and Proper Reality who descend from the In Reality/ Man o' War line were two more Claiborne stallions that interested me. As a racing fan and handicapper, I tend to think of the In Reality line as siring precocious two- and three-year-olds that don't normally stretch out to classic distances. "Not with sons of Relaunch." Seth partially qualified my opinion. "Waquoit and Skywalker got better as they got older and won a lot of route races. But on the whole, I think it's fair to say that the In Reality line is basically a speed line. Proper Reality was basically a speed horse. He won the Metropolitan, which is a mile. That's what basically drew me to him. The people that own him, the Winns, are real nice people and they're going to support him with their mares, so we're happy to have him here."

Demons Begone, a half brother to Preakness winner Pine Bluff, is an interesting example of the transformation of a sire line. As a descendant of the Chaucer/Bois Roussel branch of the St. Simon line, one would think Demons Begone would be a potential source of stamina. Seth disagreed by pointing to his immediate male ancestors. "He's probably gonna get fast horses. He's by Elocutionist who's by Gallant Romeo. That's gonna take the stamina out of that line. Because in my mind a stallion is gonna gravitate more toward his male line, not toward the female line. Whereas I think a mare will come closer to going back to her female roots. If you were talking about a full sister to Demons Begone, I'd say, yeah, there's a very good chance she might get route horses because she'll have more of a tendency to follow Rowdy Angel and her female family."

The development of good female families and maintaining the quality of Claiborne's broodmare band is, of course, one of Seth Hancock's prime responsibilities and begins when the filly foals are born. He explained the selection process. "When our fillies leave here as yearlings, we know them. We've bred them right here on the farm. They've been raised and broken here and we know all about their families. So when they leave here I can pretty much tell you that, if this one doesn't win a stake, she ain't coming back. If that one breaks her maiden, we'll take her back. If this other one can't outrun you, Mike, I'm still gonna take her back because she's out of one of our best-producing mares. That kind of filly we'll give three or four chances to and see what her foals look like. If we don't like the foals, we'll sell her then. But chances are we might like the foals and keep going with her."

Seth Hancock, of course, has made a few mistakes along the way. Early in his career, when the farm was selling most of its horses, he sold one of Special's daughters, Fairy Bridge, who subsequently produced the top European stallion Sadler's Wells. Still, the farm can't afford to keep every mare. Between the Claiborne-owned mares and those co-owned with William Haggin Perry, Seth has sixty to seventy new foals to contend with each year. Since half of those are going to be fillies, how does he decide which ones to bring back as broodmares, especially if ten or twelve of them do well at the track?

"Any mare that's a Graded Stakes winner automatically comes back." Seth further refined his broodmare citeria. "That's a lay down, a no-doubter. We normally don't have a problem with too many brood-mares because every year we sell three or four mares at the November Sale. And every year a mare or two that's been a wonderful producer gets too old to breed anymore and we'll retire her. And then every year there's unfortunately going to be a mare or two that unexpectedly dies. Last year, for example, we lost Endear, the dam of Lure, to lightning. Still, we know the number of mares we want to stay at and we always seem to stay at that number without concentrating on getting there. It just happens that way. If our numbers went up because we had a bunch of good new broodmare prospects, I wouldn't worry about it. But our standards are pretty high, so normally we don't have ten new good prospects."

Given his druthers, Seth Hancock also prefers broodmares that have shown distance ability. "I'd rather have a mare that could run a route of ground," he explained, "because it broadens your horizons. A mare like that you can breed to just about any stallion here at the farm. Whereas if you have a mare that's a pure sprinter, I'd be somewhat limited in terms of what I could breed her to because, as we talked earlier, we're a little bit limited on our stamina sources."

As a northern California racing fan, I'd followed Brown Bess during her Eclipse Award–winning year and wondered what Seth thought about her. "She's got absolutely no pedigree," he cautioned about the daughter of Petrone out of a Windy Sands mare.

"Well, then, where did she get her ability to run?" I asked.

"I'm not smart enough to figure that out," Seth retorted in a deadpan way that made me laugh. I knew that Brown Bess had subsequently been bred to Al Mamoon at Cardiff Stud Farms and asked Seth what he thought of that.

"Al Mamoon's got a shot. He's by Believe It out of a helluva mare and he had some ability. So Al Mamoon could make it."

What about California breeding in general? Most knowledgeable horse people believe that Kentucky is where it's at. If a stallion isn't standing in Kentucky, they reason, it must be because he isn't good enough to stand there. Nevertheless, I asked Seth if he thought a great stallion might make it in California or Florida.

"They have numbers going for them. I mean, as bad a golfer as I am, you give me five hundred chances on a 150-yard shot and I might hole one of them. They're breeding a lot of horses in Florida and California, and I know there are people in those two states who really know how to raise good horses. So, hell, they're dangerous. But you're going to get your better percentage of winners out of a place like Kentucky where you've got a lot better stallions, not to mention the best mares in the world. Like I said early on, you've got to have them both. It don't make any difference if you've got Mr. Prospector, you take him to Kansas and breed him to a bunch of inferior mares and you'll never hear of Mr. Prospector. I just don't think a stallion can overcome bad mares."

What about all the state-bred incentive programs that give preferential treatment to local horsemen? How much does that hurt Kentucky in terms of the number of horses it breeds and sells? "It hurts us some. Our present governor is trying to put together a $3.5 million program so Kentucky-breds will earn more when they win a race. But it's not going to be a restricted program. Those races will be open to horses bred from any state. But if a horse from Kentucky wins or is in the money, he gets 10 percent of what he would have won tacked on to that figure."

When I talked with John Mabee, the owner of Golden Eagle Farm, he told me he was in favor of unrestricted races. While in favor of state-bred incentives, he thought open competition is needed to avoid breeding mediocre horses. "Well, Best Pal is a Cal-bred," Seth observed. "How in the hell are you going to knock him? Of course, you're never going to know Best Pal is a good horse until he wins those nice *open* races. You're not going to know it by winning the seventh race on Cal Cup Day in the fall."

While the syndication of stallions was the rage in the 1970s and 1980s, the bloodstock market has dramatically changed in the tough economic climate of the 1990s. "Nobody is really thinking long term anymore," Seth explained. "Money is so tight that people are just going year to year. So syndicating a horse would be awful tough right now. Almost all of our older stallions are syndicated, but our younger ones like Ogygian, Forty Niner, Ferdinand, Proper Reality, and Academy Award aren't. Starting with about 1987, people more or less just quit syndicating horses because it got very difficult to do."

The collapse of the syndication market has, however, had some advantages. Not only does it allow for lower initial stud fees, but as Seth pointed out, "It also gives you greater control over the mares. I'd much rather handle a horse that's not syndicated than one that is."

Flexibility in setting the initial stud fee is important to any stallion manager because it allows him to peg the fee at a level that attracts a wide range of mares. "If I only get fifty mare nominations because it's a syndication or the stud fee is too high," Seth explained, "then I have to take them all. But if we set the stud fee low enough to where I get two hundred nominations, now I've got a chance to approve the *best* mares. If I can pick well, we have a better shot at increasing that stallion's chances of success."

An additional danger of initially setting a stallion's fee too high is that he may not fill his book. "That's right," Seth agreed. "On the other hand, you really can't set your stud fee too low. Because if you set it too low, that's just going to give you a great big opportunity to make the horse successful. If a horse starts at a $4,000 to $5,000 stud fee and you make him a success by the time he's ten, you've still got lots of time to make all the money that you need to make. If you start a horse like Danzig out at $20,000, maybe you set it too low. Maybe you should have put it at $25,000. But when he gets to be ten or eleven years old and he's standing for $250,000, what's the difference?"

I've always been mystified why someone would pay a lot of money for a no-guarantee season to a stallion. I asked Seth if he would ever do that. "No, that's pretty much gone now. The only horse we have around here that demands a no guarantee is Mr. Prospector, and he's twenty-two years old and everybody realizes there's not going to be many more of him. If they want to breed to him, they are going to have to pay whatever the shareholders demand. And the syndicate members are the ones that have all the seasons tied up. There are enough people who want to breed to Mr. Prospector that they'll step up to the plate and pay that big no-guarantee fee."

Throughout much of its history, Claiborne primarily bred its horses for the commercial market rather than racing them under its own silks. Seth explained some of the factors that governed that choice. "Well, my grandfather sold commercially and kind of passed it on to my father that he'd do it. Then my father did it until he got the farm on a real firm foundation to where he didn't have to sell commercially and then he pretty much stopped. He left it in his will that we do it because he knew it was a risky thing to try to race your own horses. So we sold our horses for about eight years and then felt like we were successful enough to where we could make a go of it without being commercial breeders. We stopped selling most of our crop in 1980 and have been primarily racing ever since."

Given the loss of immediate cash income, what are the advantages to Claiborne of not selling its horses? "One of the big advantages"— Seth pointed toward the stallion paddock area—"is that we have the income from Forty Niner standing out there. Whereas if we were commercial breeders, Forty Niner might well be standing someplace else. Also, a lot of our mares wouldn't be here either if we were commercial breeders because they would have been sold. It's fairly risky keeping a filly or two every year because you never really know which ones are gonna make the good race mares. If you're in it for the long haul, like we are, and trying to develop families, it's a helluva lot easier to do when you control your own destiny as opposed to taking them up there and selling them to some guy who might not give them the best chance to make it. The horses that we keep I know are gonna be trained by Shug McGaughey, Steve Penrod, and Dick Mandella. And if those guys can't make winners out of 'em, they ain't gonna be winners. Whereas if I breed thirty to forty foals every year and I send them up to the sales and the guy comes back to the farm and says, 'Well, they brought $100,000,' and I asked, 'Who bought him?' And he says, 'I don't know, some guy that races at Ruidoso Downs.' A horse might go out there and you'd never hear of him again. And I wouldn't know whether he even had a chance to be a good horse or not."

While Seth had pointed out the considerable financial advantages to Claiborne of standing a homebred like Forty Niner over managing a syndicated stallion, he also stressed that "Profit's not a word that we like to think about around here. This is a sport to us and it's been the lifeblood of this family for the last hundred years. You can look around and see this land is worth a lot of money. We're not poor people, but we don't care about being real rich people either. We've got everything that we want and we just want to try and raise good horses. If we can do that we're gonna be rich. If we were in this thing for the profit we'd probably take 'em all up there and sell them. And just keep a couple of fillies back every year. But the thrill of it for us is to breed, raise, and then run some good horses. That's what we're trying to do. If we were in it for profit we'd take the four seasons we get for Mr. Prospector every year, sell them for no guarantee, and put the money in the bank."

What about Claiborne's long-standing agreement with William Haggin Perry and his Gamely Corporation? Was the initial attraction of the partnership to spread the cost so the farm could afford to run its horses? "Well, Daddy started the agreement with Mr. Perry way back when, to kind of spread the cost. Now there's thirty mares that we own in partnership. So it's just like any partnership, he pays his half, we pay ours, and down the road we go and hope we have some luck."

While Seth Hancock spends a lot of his time managing other people's mares and stallions, his own personal breeding philosophy particularly interested me. How, for instance, does he decide which of his mares to send to which stallions? "Well, you've probably heard the old expression, 'Breed the best to the best and hope for the best.' I'm pretty much a proponent of that theory," he stated. "What I do is get the mares and rate them all on a one-to-three basis. The ones being the best, the twos next, and the threes the least attractive in terms of pedigree, conformation, and race record. Those that have all three are the ones, those that have two out of three basically are the twos, and those that only have one of them are the threes. The studs I rate the same way. Mr. Prospector, Nijinsky, Private Account, Danzig, maybe a couple more are the ones. A bunch are twos and then Demons Begone, Academy Award, and Buckfinder are the threes. What I do is match the ones to the ones, the twos to the twos, and the threes to the threes. Basically that's how I do it, paying some attention to the nicks and a helluva lot of attention to the conformation. I think that's one thing that makes a nick. People say, You're breeding Nijinsky to Round Table mares; that's a great nick. Bloodline-wise it obviously is a great nick, but what makes it a good nick is that the Nijinskys are a certain body type and the Round Table mares are a certain body type and those two types fit well together."

What about body size? Is Seth Hancock a believer in producing an average-size horse? "I know some people say you should breed type to type. In some instances I agree with that. But I think when you're first starting out with a mare, you better try to breed a balanced athlete. You go about doing that however in your mind you see fit. If she's a big mare, I don't think you breed her to a great big horse because I think you'll get an elephant and I don't think that's the kind of athlete that we're looking for. I prefer a 16-hand, well-balanced horse as opposed to some son of a gun that's 16.3 hands and looks like a giraffe."

What determines the size of a foal, of course, depends on the specific parents and varies from mating to mating, and breeders don't always wind up with what they expect. In Risen Star's case, Arthur Hancock had told me, his dam Ribbon's influence had been dominant. "Ribbon was a great big mare and his daddy Secretariat wasn't that big. He was thick but not that tall. Secretariat didn't normally sire big horses. It's interesting. Some horses can be big and sire little horses and some mares can be small and throw big horses. I think you sometimes get a genetic anomaly. You'll see a horse that's a little stallion that will sire a big horse. Nijinsky is an example of that. Northern Dancer wasn't a big horse and yet he got Nijinsky, who's a great big horse. So if you're buying a yearling, you might want to look for the genetic anomaly."

Besides being unathletic early, bigger horses also seem to have more problems in terms of injuries. Seth Hancock sees this as probably a function of having to carry more weight. "It's just common sense. If you and I have the same kind of leg and you're carrying 250 and I'm carrying 175, you're gonna break down quicker than I am. That pounding is gonna get to you. I've always thought Easy Goer had such great action that he never even pounded. He just glided."

Since Easy Goer has a poor front end, it seems surprising he ran so smoothly. "He has one foot that doesn't look that great," Seth acknowledged. "But I don't think it ever really bothered him because he had such good action. He had the reputation of being a big horse, but he really isn't that big. He's a bigger, more muscular horse than Sunday Silence, but size-wise I think they're about the same."

As a racing fan, I was disappointed when Sunday Silence went to Japan and asked Seth if that was because American breeders didn't believe he would make a good stallion. I'd heard that breeders didn't like his female family. "I don't think my brother Arthur was getting a real good reception to him," Seth responded diplomatically, "and I think that's why he made the decision to sell him. But I really don't know. You should ask Arthur."

Sunday Silence's sale to Japan had particularly bothered me because he was such an exciting racehorse, and once stallions go there they just seem to disappear. "They used to disappear," Arthur Hancock acknowledged when I talked to him. "Twenty years ago Japan had no good broodmares. But they've got them now because they bought them here and in England. So Sunday Silence may get as good a book of mares in Japan as he would have here. So maybe, from now on, we will hear about Japanese stallions."

Of course, the ultimate test for Japan's $32 billion horse industry would be for them to send their best Thoroughbreds over here to compete, something they thus far have been reluctant to do. "Well, their purses are so big over there," Arthur reflected, "that maybe they don't need to compete here. If you can run for $5 million there, why come over here? But if they get a champion-level horse, they'll probably want to do it because they obviously like to beat people at whatever they do."

Still, that didn't answer the question of why Sunday Silence isn't standing in the United States. "I wish I could have stood him," Arthur lamented. "But the Japanese offered us $10 million dollars, cash. I called thirty to thirty-five of the best breeders in the world and only three people, Josephine Abercrombie, Watts Humphrey, and Richard Duchossois, indicated they'd take a share. They were the only people that would take one at $250,000 a share, and that was payable over four years with a prime interest rate of around nine percent. So I got three takers. We had forty shares—me and Charlie Whittingham and Dr. Gaillard. Given that, you'd have to be a fool not to take the $10 million. So we sold him. Even though I was compensated for my breeding rights, to have had Sunday Silence stand here would have been fantastic. To be able to breed to him. The publicity you get, the image for your farm, and so forth. But that's just what we had to do. Of course, given what's happened to the bloodstock market since, maybe it was a blessing. Now you couldn't stand Sunday Silence for $25,000, which would make him have a value at forty shares of maybe $4 million. So I have to think that was one of the best sales ever made in the bloodstock industry. Still, I hated doing it. It nearly killed me. I stayed up almost all of one night just sitting over there in that chair thinking. I'll never forget going over to the barn the day Sunday Silence was leaving. I just went up to his stall door and stood there. He looked at me almost as if he knew. And then the van came. It was like losing a member of the family. So I repeated the old saying: 'There's two things you don't want to fall in love with, and that's a whore and a horse because they'll both break your heart.' I always try to remember that."

Back with Seth Hancock, I asked him if he was concerned about the increasing number of American stallions going to Japan in recent years. What long-run effect, if any, does he think it will have on the quality of the American stud? "If you see the Forty Niners, the Alyshebas, the Gulches, and those kind going over there, that would have a big effect," he agreed. "But most of the ones that have gone haven't been our top prospects. So far, I don't think they've made much of a dent into the male population. They have made a dent in the female population."

What about the Claiborne tradition of importing some of Europe's better stallions? Couldn't a horse like Caerleon command a much bigger stud fee and get better mares over here rather than standing in Ireland? "That's true," Seth reflected, "but there aren't that many Caerleons in Europe. So he's the extreme big fish in a small pond over there. Whereas if he comes over here, he's gonna be thrown into a pool with a lot of real good stallions."

In recent years a number of pedigree scholars have become concerned that, with the ubiquitous interbreeding among the speedy Raise a Native, Bold Ruler, and Northern Dancer lines, the gene pool of the Thoroughbred is getting shorter and shorter. Additionally, with fewer opportunities, the survival of many formerly prominent non-

Phalaris bloodlines such as those of Hyperion, Tourbillon, Chaucer, Blenheim, Sir Gallahad, and Domino is now increasingly dependent on the success of one or two descendants. Does maintaining genetic diversity within the breed concern Seth Hancock?

"It does," he replied. "But it goes back to the situation I was in with Festin. What am I gonna do about it? I'm not gonna go busted trying to make it another way. I mean, I could stand Festin and go to Argentina and get another horse that is a complete outcross and bring him in here and breed him to ten of our best mares and I could spread that gene pool out and make it go the other way. But if I breed twenty bad horses from those ten matings to those two horses, I've screwed up big time. Right now I don't have enough confidence in the Festins of the world to go out and do something like that. If I could get forty guys to all breed one and we could share the risk, that'd be fine. I could have got some mares to a horse like that, but I don't think they'd have been the kind of mares that would have ensured that he'd have had every chance to be successful. And if I can't do that, then I'm robbing Festin of his chance at glory and I would never want to do that. But that's just me. I'm not a great salesman. My brother Arthur is a terrific salesman. That's where Festin is and he'll do a helluva lot better job with him than I could."

I liked Seth's idea of sharing the risk of standing more stamina-oriented stallions. In fact, it reminded me of a number of conversations that I'd had with Rommy Faversham, a southern California M.D. and pedigree analyst who contributes to Jack Werk's *Owner/Breeder* magazine. Faversham is similarly concerned that the Thoroughbred gene pool has not only been losing its diversity but, with the bias toward speed and precocity, been getting shorter and shorter. He believes the big horse farms such as Claiborne, Gainesway, and Lane's End, which stand twenty or more stallions, are the only ones that can afford the risk of standing stouter, less commercial stallions. He thinks it would be great if they each stood at least one non-Phalaris, preferably stamina-oriented horse as an outcross to the dominant Raise a Native, Northern Dancer, and Bold Ruler blood. Faversham doesn't think they have to breed forty or fifty mares to them, just enough to keep threatened lines alive and thus maintain a broader gene pool. Even if contemporary descendants of Domino, Himyar, Tourbillon, Rock Sand,

Dark Ronald, Blenheim, Hyperion, and Princequillo don't produce great sons, he argues, they are important to keep in the gene pool as broodmare sires.

I liked Faversham's idea but told him I thought that racing secretaries, in conjunction with maybe the Jockey Club or some other sponsors, also had to start writing longer races with decent purses, so there would be an economic incentive for breeders to breed more stamina into some of their horses. Interestingly, there is evidence that racing fans prefer a greater diversity in the daily card. Robert Umphrey, when he was the racing secretary at Golden Gate Fields, for instance, told me that the track's biggest handle was on the longer turf races. Nevertheless, Rommy Faversham still feels it's the breeder's responsibility to do the job first and that racetracks will then follow. Otherwise, he predicts, racing secretaries will never write longer races.

"Racing secretaries probably won't write longer races," Seth Hancock agreed, "because then they'll have five-horse fields and it won't be a good betting race and that type of thing. The only thing I can tell you is that nobody's more aware of what you're talking about than I am. But I look down that roster of Belmont winners—and I'm sure that it's the greatest stamina race we have. I mean, it's a mile and a half—and I just see those Belmont winners have not made real good sires and that scares me. I look at the Metropolitan Mile and its roster of winners and I see that a big, big number of those winners make very good sires. Cox's Ridge won the Metropolitan and he had no right whatsoever to make a good sire, but he has. And he's a good sire of stamina too. Conquistador Cielo won the Metropolitan. You get ahold of a list of Metropolitan winners and it's just amazing how many good sires have come out of it. It's a race for older horses run toward the end of May on Memorial Day. In my mind it's been the most productive race for picking future sires."

Seth's observation about the Metropolitan was interesting because turf scholars like Abram Hewitt have similarly concluded that good milers tend to make the best sires. "I really think they do," Seth said. "Milers have to have a good deal of speed, but also a certain amount of stamina. Pure out-and-out sprinters don't win going a mile. I don't like pure out-and-out sprinters. I mean, if I thought that speed was the absolute key to the thing, I'd go get the Breeders' Cup Sprint winner every year and that would be the only horse that you would retire to stud. And I'm not taking anything away from those kind of horses. I think Housebuster is a good prospect as a sire. But he was also a good miler."

Housebuster is an interesting horse because he is a descendant of Nasrullah through Red God and Blushing Groom. With such prominent sons as Rainbow Quest, Crystal Glitters, Blushing John, Nashwan, Mt. Livermore, Rahy, and now his grandson Housebuster at stud, an increasing number of pedigree analysts are predicting that the Nasrullah line will more likely be carried on through Blushing Groom than Bold Ruler.

"I think the Blushing Groom line will be very prominent," Seth partially agreed. "Nashwan is a terrific sire prospect. But it's way too early to write off Bold Ruler. Seattle Slew has a couple of good sons in Slew o' Gold and Capote and he'll have some more."

While Slew o' Gold got a distance and might sire a Classic-winning son, I wondered about Capote. "I don't think he will get horses that will route," Seth predicted. "He's out of a mare called Too Bald who's by Bald Eagle. She had a horse called Baldski that was by Nijinsky. Baldski just made a *chef-de-race* and he's a sprint sire. So now if Too Bald can't get anything but a sprint sire by Nijinsky, she ain't going to get a horse that sires route horses by Seattle Slew, in my opinion."

With Blushing Groom's son Arazi all but conceded the Triple Crown by the pundits, I was curious how Seth saw the upcoming three-year-old Classics. "Well, Arazi looks like a standout off of one race. But he's got a lot to overcome. He's got knee surgery to overcome. The fact that he's going to be trained in France and then shipped over here. I think that A. P. Indy would probably be my pick for the Classics. He's trained by a guy, Neil Drysdale, that can train a horse to get a route of ground, that's a very good trainer. He's got a really good sit-still, waiting rider in Delahousaye. He's got a great pedigree and was raised at a great farm. So I'd give him a strong look for the Classics."

Chalk one up for Seth Hancock! While Arazi unleashed a bold move in the Kentucky Derby, he hung badly and left the strong impression that he might be merely a fast-closing miler. A. P. Indy's victory in the Belmont and in the Breeders' Cup Classic against older horses, however, clearly proved him a superior racehorse. By Triple Crown champion Seattle Slew and out of a mare by Triple Crown champion Secretariat, A. P. Indy, in Seth's opinion, "has a helluva shot as a stallion prospect and we're sending a Mr. Prospector mare to him."

Another sire line that recently has seen a resurgence is that of Icecapade, a stallion often referred to as the poor man's Northern Dancer. By Nearctic and out of the Native Dancer mare Shenanigans, Icecapade's pedigree is very similar to Northern Dancer's because they both had the same sire and broodmare sire. Given that sons of Icecapade like Phone Trick and Wild Again have tended to sire precocious two-year-olds, I guessed that Seth would be partial to them.

"They've been great," he agreed. "I'm surprised. I'd be the first to admit that. But with what Wild Again and Clever Trick have done and now Phone Trick, I think Icecapade is terrific, what's going on there. It's basically a speed line. I don't think there's going to be any real Cup horses to come from there. But otherwise it's a terrific sire line."

Our conversation shifted back to Forty Niner. "I'm very interested in the race for the freshman sire," Seth volunteered. "This year the leading players should be Alysheba, Gulch, and Forty Niner. That'll be interesting. Personally, I like Forty Niner, but no doubt I'm a little bit prejudiced. Gulch was precocious at two and Alysheba is the leading money winner of all time, with a good pedigree and at a good farm. He's got a great big chance to make it."

When he was racing, Alysheba struck me as being fairly big. I wondered if that wouldn't compromise his chances as a sire of two-year-olds. "Well, I agree with what you're saying," Seth responded. "It wouldn't surprise me if they didn't come out really smoking, but who knows."

Forty Niner, on the other hand, was a champion two-year-old and, judging by the prices his yearlings have fetched, is much more likely to get precocious runners. Whether his get will stretch out to Classic distances at three, it seemed to me, would depend a lot on what kind of mares he's been bred to.

"I agree with you," Seth responded. "So far Forty Niner's gotten a lot of Northern Dancer–line mares—Nijinsky, Northern Dancer him-self, Danzig, Lyphard—he's gotten a lot of that blood. I don't know if that will help him to stretch out. He's not going to be a Pleasant Colony–type horse and win the Jockey Gold Cup. But then he'll have more stamina than a horse like Capote. He's from File, a mare by Tom Rolfe. He's from the St. Simon line that you mentioned is really the one that's stamina-oriented and I couldn't agree with you more. And you're looking right there at Tom Rolfe and Ribot in Forty Niner's female family. I mean, if you want to carry it a step further, he's the same color as his mother, not the same color as his father. So he must have inherited a lot of his mother's genes."

On the surface, the pedigrees of Forty Niner and Majestic Light seemed similar. They both come out of Ribot-line mares and are by Raise a Native–line sires. I wondered if Forty Niner might become the same kind of sire as Majestic Light. "They were such different types as racehorses," Seth Hancock disagreed. "I don't think Majestic Light did much as a two-year-old. He was better going a route of ground, and in his races he settled a little ways off the pace and then made a great big run. Whereas Forty Niner was right on top of the pace in all of his races. So he had a lot more turn of foot than Majestic Light. Majestic Light gets route and turf horses, and I'm sure a lot of that has to do with the type of horse he was and his pedigree. But Forty Niner has a route pedigree and I wouldn't worry about him getting only sprinters."

Majestic Light also interested me because he is the sire of Simply Majestic, a speed horse that burned up the track in northern Califor-nia going as far as 1⅛ mile and finished a close third on the turf in the Breeders' Cup Mile. He also won eighteen of forty-four starts and nearly $1.7 million. I asked Seth what he thought of him as a sire prospect. "Not too much." He shook his head. "I wouldn't like Simply Majestic."

"Why not? Because of his female family?" I queried.

"Yeah, a lot of it. He's out of a mare by King Emperor and he was basically a flop as a sire."

"So if the broodmare sire is a flop, that turns you off to the female family?"

"No, not really. Two of our best sires, Cox's Ridge and Danzig, had broodmare sires that didn't make it. Cox's Ridge is out of a Ballydonnell mare and Danzig's out of an Admiral's Voyage mare and both of those, as far as my experience goes, were basically unsuccessful stallions. So when I look at Simply Majestic, the broodmare sire isn't what stops me as much as the actual immediate females from that family and what they've been able to produce."

Since good female families are so important, which mares does Seth consider to be the foundation ones for Claiborne's broodmare band? "The Bourtai family through Delta and all her daughters, that's been a big family for us. Bourtai was the dam of Bayou, who was the dam of Alluvial. Then Knights Daughter was the dam of Monarchy, who was the dam of State. We have a lot of that family. Rough Shod was the dam of Thong, who was the dam of Special, and Rough Shod was also the dam of Moccasin, so we have a lot of that family. Then there's Continue, the dam of File. We have four daughters of File here. That will be an important family for us. Iskra, the dam of Arushka, who was the dam of Find and Guild, will be a foundation mare for us. Regal Gleam, who was the dam of Foreseer, who is the dam of Far and Video, are all female families that will be important to us."

Seth's mention of Special reminded me of her broodmare sire Forli, a Hyperion-line stallion that his father imported from Argentina in 1967 and who stood at Claiborne until 1988. The sire of the great Forego, Forli has been relatively neglected as a broodmare sire in recent years even though his daughters and granddaughters have produced such outstanding horses as Swale, Precisionist, Nureyev, and Sadler's Wells. How many Forli mares, I wondered, does Claiborne still have left? "We've got Thong, Gilly, and Special. A couple of them are old, but we've still got three left," Seth stated. "So Forli's been good to us. Round Table and Herbager mares were good to us too, but they're all gone. Still, we've had luck with a lot of different stallions. Mr. Prospector has been good to us and continues to be good to us. Horses like that, that were bred to our best mares, they obviously produced daughters that are out of the best mares, so that's hopefully something that will continue on."

As successful a horseman as Seth Hancock has been over the past twenty years, I couldn't help also reflecting that he's played the racing game with the advantage of a pretty good set of cards. Given the harsh economic climate of the 1990s, I was curious what advice he would give someone just getting into breeding who had a little bit of money to play with.

"What you callin' a little bit of money?" Seth cut to the quick.

"Well, let's start at the top with a million bucks," I opened.

"I'd tell them to buy three $300,000 mares and go from there," Seth responded.

"You'd always start with the mare?"

"I would."

Suppose, on the other hand, a potential breeder has more enthusiasm than money. What's the bottom level, in Seth's opinion, that it's worth taking a shot on a mare?

"You better have $50,000." Seth implicitly warned about the dangers of going too cheap. "And if you can't afford that, then find yourself partners and buy a mare together."

Once the mare has been bought, the next question is what stud fee range to look for in a proven stallion that she might be bred to. "You can pretty much figure that the stud fee should be about a fifth of the value of the mare," Seth advised. "So if you buy a $50,000 mare, you wouldn't want to put more than a $10,000 fee in her. With a $300,000 mare, you might go a little higher and put up to $75,000 in her."

Some breeders believe you can take a cheaper mare and breed some class into her foals by going to a more expensive stallion. "I don't believe in overbreeding," Seth categorically responded. "If a mare is a good mare, she'll show it by throwing a good foal from a lesser stallion. Once she's proven she can produce a good foal from a lesser stallion, then it makes sense to invest a higher stud fee in her."

How about choosing between a proven or an unproven but promising stallion? What would govern his choice? "How much money you got." Seth minced no words. "If you can afford it, I think you're better off going to the proven stallion."

We'd covered a lot of territory and it seemed appropriate to loop back to a more personal vein. Doc Kaufman had told me out in the broodmare barn one morning that racing was finally selling one thing and that was the excitement, the dramatic tension that springs from hope. He'd told me that watching his filly No Choice win the Gardenia Stakes had been his most transcendent moment in racing. How about Seth? What single event has most fired his blood in recent years?

"Winning the Travers with Forty Niner." Seth didn't hesitate. "Probably more so even than Swale winning the Kentucky Derby. Because of the circumstances. Woody Stephens was real sick. Devil's Bag had just been retired, and it was Woody's and our first Travers win. It was a million-dollar race and the horse that was second was a farm horse. It was a pretty day weather-wise. All those things made it a really big thrill."

EPILOGUE

Nine months later, in mid-December, it seemed clear that 1992 was going to be a banner year for Claiborne. The farm had consigned the top-two-selling yearlings at the Keeneland July Sale for $1.7 and $1.3 million respectively. On the racetrack Forty Niner's first crop had performed to expectations, and he was contending for freshman sire honors. For the second year in a row Danzig looked to lead the general sire list. Secretariat, with the help of A. P. Indy's late fall move, had jumped to the top of the broodmare sire standings. And Nijinsky, with a strong assist from Sky Classic, was going out a champion as the leading turf sire. Then, as if this clean sweep of all the major breeding honors wasn't enough, Lure's theft of the Breeders' Cup Mile at Gulfstream in a sizzling 132.2 was the cherry on top of the Claiborne cake.

Of course, the farm's jubilation had also been tempered. Nijinsky, overwhelmed by his infirmities, finally had to be humanely put down by Doc Kaufman. Topsider dropped dead from a stroke. Two other stallions, Vanlandingham and Polish Navy, had been disappointments in Kentucky and been shipped off to Oklahoma and Japan. And Henryk de Kwiatkowski, after gallantly rescuing Calumet, had relocated some fifty of his broodmares from Claiborne to their new home.

With another breeding season approaching and Claiborne's broodmare and stallion populations both down, I was curious if Seth was content to downsize or preferred to buck the prevailing economic trend and build the farm's stock back up. "I'd like to build back up a little bit," he told me. "I'd like to have three hundred mares again, so we can foal two hundred mares here a year and add a few stallions so we're back up to between twenty and twenty-two on our roster."

Catching up with the rest of the news, I was intrigued by the two Mr. Prospector yearlings that had fetched $3 million at Keeneland's July Sale. Both colts, I'd noted, were out of the Nijinsky mares Number and Bound, whose dam Special (by Forli) had produced Nureyev. While these two colts were obviously bred in the purple, in looking at a foal's pedigree, I was curious how far back Seth would advise a yearling buyer to go.

"It depends on how much money you got to spend," he explained. "If you're down at the lower end, you gotta go way back to find some class. If you're at the upper end, you don't have to go too far back. But, practically, as a breeder, I go back four generations."

So, looking at those two Mr. Prospector colts out of Number and Bound, since Forli is in their third generation, would Seth consider him a significant influence in their pedigrees? "Yes. But you're also looking at Mr. Prospector, Nijinsky, and a mare like Special even closer up. That's why they brought so much."

Given Claiborne's $3 million success at the July Sale with those two colts, Seth indicated that Number and Bound would be bred back pretty much along the same lines. One mare was going back to Mr. Prospector and the other to his son, Forty Niner. Interestingly, Number and Bound both also have daughters that are now part of Claiborne's broodmare band. So the Special female family connection promises to be an important one for years to come.

226

Since Seth had previously told me that most of his Forli, Round Table, and Herbager mares were gone, the thought occurred to me that he would now be turning to his Nijinsky and Secretariat mares as the principal source of stamina in his stud. "Yes," he agreed. "You'd have to think so. Nijinsky and Secretariat mares are not only gonna provide stamina for us, but other breeders as well."

Even though Claiborne has done extremely well at the July Yearling Sale, most industry analysts have concluded that Keeneland's less expensive September Sale is becoming the most important vendue for commercial breeders. Does Seth agree? "Yes. I think in time the July Sale will have 100 to 120 yearlings and be like a champagne sale and the rest of the horses will be sold in the fall."

I'd been in the gallery at Keeneland's November Breeding Stock Sale when Seth had signed the million-dollar ticket for Wild Applause, a Graustark mare that was in foal to Forty Niner at Paul Mellon's Rokeby dispersal sale. What, I asked him, was his thinking when he bought the mare for Adele Dilschneider, a Claiborne client? How much of the mare's value came from her female family, which traces back to La Troienne, and how much from her being in foal to Forty Niner? "I just think the mare's got a helluva chance to be a good broodmare," he replied. "Her first four foals (including the stallion prospect Eastern Echo) have all been winners and showed terrific promise. And a couple of them were by less than top-flight stallions. I think she's an ideal mare for Mr. Prospector, and that's who we're going to breed her to. She hasn't had that kind of opportunity before, and I'm anxious to give it to her and see if she can't have a good horse by him. Her being in foal to Forty Niner wasn't a major consideration because we've got Forty Niner and can breed her to him whenever we want."

What about Lure's big win in the Breeders' Cup Mile? Was Seth surprised? "Not really, no. He was doing so good down there. I didn't think Arazi would run well. The firm turf, I thought, would play against him. And Lure was one of the few speed horses in the race and he had the fence. That gave him a great big chance."

I had gotten scared off the horse because he was a three-year-old. "Well, A. P. Indy and Lure both won against older horses," Seth pointed out. "I agree with you that generally it's tough for three-year-olds to beat older horses. But I think A. P. Indy was a helluva horse and let's hope Lure is, too. He sure looked to be a helluva horse that day."

Seth, of course, was pleased about Lure's win because as a home-bred son of Danzig and a Breeders' Cup Mile winner, his chances of standing at Claiborne right alongside of Forty Niner had been immeasurably enhanced. And Forty Niner, of course, was having a dynamite rookie year with thirteen winners, as of December 15, out of his first crop to race. "Forty Niner's had a great year and we're really tickled with him," Seth enthused. "He's just a little behind Silver Deputy and Gulch for freshman sire honors."

With two weeks left before the new year, I wondered if there were any races that might put Forty Niner on top. "We're workin' on it," Seth assured me. "We're only $22,000 behind the leader right now, and all his horses are Canadian horses so they're about through. And there's four or five starters left for Forty Niner. So if we get lucky in a couple of spots, he might make it." (He did!)

One of the things that surprised me, on my visits to Kentucky, was how many people at competing farms were rooting for Forty Niner. There was very little envious talk about Claiborne having all the marbles. "He's a popular horse," Seth agreed. "People seem to like him. They liked him when he was running and they like him now."

Forty Niner's popularity, in fact, was so strong that his 1993 stud fee was going up ten grand to $70,000 while stud fees throughout the industry were spiraling down. Forty Niner had proven he could get two-year-old runners and his next test would be to see if he could produce older stakes winners in 1993.

With Easy Goer's yearlings about to hit the market, I wondered if Seth was concerned with the industry view that, thus far, sons of Alydar have not been precocious sires. "Sons of Alydar definitely are on the bubble," he agreed. "And Alysheba's slow start hasn't helped. So Easy Goer will be under a lot of pressure. His first yearlings will go to Keeneland this summer, so we'll find out then what people think."

Seeking the Gold, whose first crop was about to hit the track, was being greeted with considerably more enthusiasm by people in the industry. "Well, sons of Mr. Prospector are a hot item right now," Seth explained, "and Seeking the Gold has a bunch of two-year-olds that look like runners, so we're pretty excited about what we're seeing out there. They looked good and sold well. And hopefully they're gonna run good too."

Somehow, it seemed appropriate to conclude with little Proper Reality, whose two-year-olds were about to be similarly tested on the track. As a son of In Reality and descendant of Man o' War, he comes from a less fashionable sire line than sons of Mr. Prospector, and I wondered how his foals were doing. "Well, they didn't sell well," Seth acknowledged, "but they're pretty athletic-looking. I think they'll run, but they aren't gonna be horses that sell well."

"So, since they didn't burn up the auction ring," I queried, "they'll have to make it at the track?"

"In the end, Mike"—Seth paused for emphasis—"they all do."

INDEX